Once Upon a Christmas

Once Upon
a Christmas

COMPILED BY ESTHER RANTZEN

MICHAEL JOSEPH
LONDON

MICHAEL JOSEPH LTD

Published by the Penguin Group
27 Wrights Lane, London w8 5tz
Viking Penguin Inc., 375 Hudson Street, New York, New York 10014, USA
Penguin Books Australia Ltd, Ringwood, Victoria, Australia
Penguin Books Canada Ltd, 10 Alcorn Avenue, Toronto, Ontario, Canada m4v 3b2
Penguin Books (NZ) Ltd, 182–190 Wairau Road, Auckland 10, New Zealand

Penguin Books Ltd, Registered Offices: Harmondsworth, Middlesex, England

First published 1996
5 7 9 10 8 6 4

Typeset in 10/12pt Monotype Baskerville
Designed in QuarkXpress on an Apple Macintosh
Printed in England by Clays Ltd, St Ives plc

A CIP catalogue record for this book is available from the British Library

isbn 0 7181 4141 5

Contributors

v

Acknowledgements

All royalties will be paid to ChildLine Trading Ltd which covenants all its taxable profits to ChildLine (a registered charity).

The recipe by Marco Pierre White is taken from *Canteen Cuisine* by Marco Pierre White (© 1995), reproduced by permission of Ebury Press.

The recipe by Raymond Blanc is reproduced by kind permission from *Cooking For Friends*, published by Headline.

The recipe by Michel Roux is taken from *Desserts, A Lifelong Passion* by Michel Roux, published by Conran Octopus, copyright © Michel Roux, 1994.

The recipe by Antonio Carluccio is taken from *Antonio Carluccio's Invitation to Italian Cooking*, copyright © Antonio Carluccio, 1986.

The contribution by George Melly is taken from his autobiography, *Scouse Mouse*, copyright © George Melly, 1984.

'Generations of Christmas' by Sheridan Morley first appeared in *Punch*, 5 December 1973, copyright © Sheridan Morley, 1973, reproduced by permission of *Punch*.

Foreword by
Diana Princess of Wales

Christmas is a time which can be lonely, can be sad, but it can also bring joy, laughter and light, and a time of great blessings to so many.

However, for some children who are suffering distress or pain, Christmas simply serves to underline their loneliness, so we must give them hope and show them that it is not all sadness and conflict. Child-Line is there to help these children. I am therefore delighted to have this opportunity to thank the many distinguished contributors who have added their own story or poem to this collection in order to support the work of ChildLine.

This book contains stories of Christmases past, and recipes for the perfect Christmases to come. Let us therefore make time to stop and reflect on how we can continue to make Christmas special to all children who need so much love and support at this time.

May I wish you, the readers, and the contributors, a very Happy Christmas, and to ChildLine and its team I wish every possible success in their crucial and valuable work for children who are our future.

Diana

Introduction by The Rt. Hon. John Major MP, Prime Minister

Ten years ago in October 1986 ChildLine was created. It has become literally a lifeline for children. Any child able to dial the number can speak to a ChildLine counsellor who will listen, comfort and advise. Its impact has been considerable. The voices of children who, in the past, would have suffered in silence can now be heard. Abuse has been detected, the pain of bereavement eased and drug problems solved, to highlight just a few of the areas where ChildLine has helped children.

This collection of Christmas stories, poems and recipes – all freely donated by the contributors – will help ChildLine develop its work. The royalties from its sale will mean more children can get through for the advice and help they need. ChildLine has been and will continue to be immensely valuable in protecting vulnerable children. Thank you for buying this book.

Spike Milligan

ENTERTAINER AND WRITER

Once upon a time, when I was five years old, I lived in India. My daddy was a soldier in the Indian Army and I lived with my mother and grandmother in No. 5 Old Sappers Lines, Poona, and I wanted a box of soldiers for my Christmas present.

On Christmas Eve I sat in the lounge and my grandmother read me a ghost story and then they gave me a glass of hot milk, put on my night-shirt and put me to bed. Somewhere in the early hours I woke up and I saw all my toys were in a pillowcase on my bed. It was very early and my mother and grandmother were in the room. They must have woken me when they were putting my pillowcase of toys on the bed and they wanted me to go back to sleep.

They said, 'Oh, goodness me. You have just woken up and Father Christmas has just left through that window.'

I was very puzzled because the window had chicken wire over it to stop people getting in and I wondered then how Father Christmas got through the chicken wire in one piece and got out again.

At school the next week the teacher asked us all to draw a picture of Father Christmas. I drew a Father Christmas with a thousand spots as if he had come through the chicken wire in thousands of pieces. When my teacher asked me why I had drawn Father Christmas in thousands of pieces, I told her that is how he got through the chicken wire. My teacher looked at me very strangely.

And for many years at Christmas until I grew up I thought Father Christmas could get through a window covered in chicken wire but I never doubted what my mother and grandmother had said.

That is a Christmas which I shall never forget.

Marco Pierre White

CHEF

FILLET OF BEEF FORESTIÈRE, POMME RÖSTI, MADEIRA SAUCE

This dish is expensive, using four fillet steaks, but we like to offer it occasionally at the Canteen – it's one of our specials.

To ensure a good shape to your steaks, buy the fillet in one piece. Wrap it in cling film, roll out evenly, and chill to 'set' for twenty-four hours. Cut into steaks, then pan-fry with the cling film still in place around the outside diameter. Remove the cling film before serving.

For the Pomme Rösti, try to use a potato such as Désirée that will crisp up well.

SERVES 4
4 × 175 g (6 oz) fillet steaks, trimmed
salt and freshly ground white pepper
100 ml (3½ fl oz) vegetable oil

WILD MUSHROOMS
100 g (4 oz) mixed wild mushrooms (preferably morels, girolles, ceps and trompettes de mort) according to season
75 g (3 oz) unsalted butter
1 shallot, peeled and finely chopped
1 tomato, skinned, seeded and diced
1 teaspoon snipped chives

TO SERVE
1 recipe Pomme Rösti (see below)
1 recipe Madeira Sauce (see below)

1. Make the pomme rösti and the sauce, and keep warm.
2. Wash and prepare the mushrooms, then separately sauté each in 15g (½ oz) of the butter. (This can be done about 1 hour in advance.)
3. When ready to finally cook and serve, season the steaks and pan-fry in the oil until cooked to your liking – preferably medium rare, about 3–4 minutes on each side, but depending on thickness. You could fry it for a shorter time, then flash into a well preheated hot oven, at 250°C/500°F/the highest gas, for a minute or two.
4. Reheat the mushrooms by sautéing them in the remaining butter with the shallot. Add the diced tomato, chives and seasoning at the last moment.
5. To serve, place a pomme rösti on each plate, with a steak on top. Arrange the mushrooms around the steak, and pour the sauce over.

POMME RÖSTI

2 large Désirée potatoes
salt
50 g (2 oz) clarified butter

1. Peel the potatoes, slice them finely, then cut into julienne strips, neither too thick nor too thin.
2. Salt the strips and leave hanging in a cloth for the liquid to drip out. Squeeze to get the potato strips as dry as possible.
3. Mix the dried potato with warm clarified butter.
4. There are several ways of proceeding now. If you have an electric or solid-fuel hob, divide the potato between four Tefal galette moulds of 7.5 cm (3 in) in diameter. Press down evenly and then place the bottom of the mould over the heat. The heat must not be too high (or the base of the rösti will burn and the inside will not be cooked) or too low. Cook for 5–7 minutes altogether.
5. Or, on other hobs, use a non-stick frying pan with similar-sized round cutters. Push the potato into them, smooth and then fry first one side, then, pushing down again, the other.
  You could, of course, just cook in tablespoonfuls, but you really want that nice even shape.

MADEIRA SAUCE

1 tbsp vegetable oil
100 g (4 oz) pie veal, chopped
3 shallots, peeled and finely sliced
40 g (1½ oz) mushrooms, sliced
2 large garlic cloves, peeled and sliced in half
1 small sprig thyme
¼ bay leaf
1 tbsp sherry vinegar
1 tbsp Cognac
325 ml (11 fl oz) Madeira
325 ml (11 fl oz) veal stock
75 ml (2½ fl oz) chicken stock
50 ml (2 fl oz) water

1. Heat the oil in a large frying pan over a moderate heat and sauté the meat for about 10 minutes, turning it occasionally, until golden brown all over.

2. Add the shallot, mushrooms, garlic, thyme and bay leaf, and continue to cook for about 5 minutes, stirring frequently, until all the liquid from the mushrooms has gone.

3. Add the vinegar and continue to cook until the liquid has evaporated, then deglaze with the Cognac, pouring it around the outside of the pan. Pour in the Madeira and cook rapidly to reduce it by about four-fifths.

4. Add the stock and the water, stir and bring to the boil. Reduce the heat and simmer for 20 minutes, removing any scum that appears from time to time. Pass through a muslin-lined sieve three times, rinsing the muslin each time.

Richard Branson

BUSINESSMAN

A CHRISTMAS TALE

The best gifts that we can receive at Christmas are not the toys, or toasters or tea-towels that we give one another – as nice as they may be – but the less obvious gifts of friendship and family. It's easy to take these for granted, but they can sometimes arrive when you least expect them.

In 1968, some friends and I were running a magazine called *Student*, and decided to set up the Student Advisory Centre. In those days there seemed to be far fewer places where young people could go for advice on problems about contraception, housing, legal or financial matters and we were quickly inundated with enquiries and callers.

Our 'office' was in a house in West London, which was owned by the Church Commissioners, who took exception to the fact that their property had been turned into an extension of the social services, and asked us to leave.

Christmas was coming, and we found ourselves out on the street, with nowhere to go, when an angel came to our rescue. Cuthbert Scott was the vicar of the local church, St John's. He heard about our problem and offered us the use of the crypt for the Advisory Centre. It was a very welcome Christmas present. The crypt had not been opened since being used as an air-raid shelter during the war; it was dank and cluttered, but we set to cleaning it up and, thanks to Cuthbert, we were able to continue with our work.

We stayed open day and night, and there was sometimes confusion between the distressed students coming in for advice and the rather well-to-do young mothers and nannies using the nursery in the church hall, but Cuthbert took it all in his stride. Shortly afterwards, Cuthbert left to move to another parish. He had been a great friend to the Advisory Centre, and I was extremely sorry to see him go. I didn't know whether I would see him again.

A week later, I went down to the country to see my family for Christmas. Christmas was always a very special occasion for us, my parents, my two sisters and me, with the house full of friends. On Christmas Eve my mother announced that we had a new vicar in the parish and he would be calling in that afternoon to say hello. When the doorbell rang later, I answered it. Standing there was the new vicar, and – of course – it was Cuthbert Scott. We were both overjoyed to see each other again, and it made a happy Christmas a perfect one.

We continued to stay in touch after that, and have become firm friends. Cuthbert has retired now, but, thanks to him, the Student Advisory Centre goes on. As I say, the best presents are often the ones you least expect.

Phillip Schofield

BROADCASTER

I lived in New Zealand with my family for about four years, between 1980 and 1984. It was my dad's idea to emigrate. He had always wondered what it would be like to live there so, rather than go for a holiday, we went to live. We being Mum, Dad, brother Tim and I.

To get into New Zealand all four of us had to undergo rigorous questioning about why we wanted to go and what we expected once we got there. At the end of that lengthy session we were asked if we had any questions. That was when the mistake was made: not one of us dreamed to ask about Christmas. Would you?

We arrived in New Zealand in September of 1980. Twelve thousand miles between us and Britain, about as far as you can go without coming back! What a country, with so many new and different things to experience. Every day brought another exciting discovery. From the scariest tree creature you've ever seen, the weta, native only to New Zealand (thank goodness), to the revelation that the water in the Southern Hemisphere goes down the plug hole in the opposite direction to Britain. My brother Tim and I were thirsty for knowledge and we were having a very satisfying drink.

As the months rolled by and we began to think about Christmas, we also became aware that it was getting hotter. We knew that summers 'down under' are the opposite to back home, with the hottest months between November and February. Still the penny didn't drop and at the beginning of December we began to look for a turkey.

It's probably important at this time to explain just what the Schofields are like during the season of goodwill. We love it, every little bit of it. Robins sitting on spades, a Christmas tree that would make a Mountie homesick, chestnuts exploding into thousands of little pieces in the fireplace, snow, tinsel, holly dripping with scarlet berries, even that terrible moment when you know that, to put your cracker hat on, you're going to have to split it because your head's too big! Every single tradition is inhaled in great, hearty, pine-scented lungfuls in our house, and if it's snowing outside, well that's the icing on the log.

So, back to December in the Antipodes, where the temperature was in the high 80s and steadily rising. We turned down, with an indignant sniff, the invitations to two Christmas beach barbies. And with a great deal of investigative work a sad and sorry turkey was tracked down and ordered from a man who, for some reason, kept sniggering down the telephone. As the sweat dripped from our brows, we, the only diehard festive traditionalist Brits in Auckland, having failed to find any holly, hung up the Pohutukawa.

We are, I think, quite a calm family. Usually it's not such a task for us to remain steadfast under pressure, but as the sun rose over Auckland on 25 December 1980, our resolve was finally about to crack. By 11 a.m. we had opened all our presents and started on the Quality Street. The signs were all there to be seen, if only we had looked. Those yellow toffee chewy ones that nobody eats were beginning to melt.

By high noon the screams coming from the kitchen were too much to bear. Mum had refused all help on a number of occasions and it was becoming obvious that somebody had to get her out of there. It was 92 in the shade and she was screaming abuse at the sprouts. Windows were opened to try and catch even the smallest passing breeze. Sweat was running as easily as the insults and then, suddenly, it all stopped . . . in slow motion we saw Mum, bright pink and wearing only a T-shirt and pants, with a fuse about as short as Willie Carson's jodhpurs, open the oven door. As she bent down to pick out the roast potatoes a tiny trickle of sweat made its devastating journey south. Slipping unnoticed, it crossed her forehead and headed for her eyebrows. Her hands were now on the baking tray. The tiny bead dodged back and forth between the hairs of her brows and made a headlong dash for her eye. Just as the potatoes were at waist height, the stinging, salty bead jumped into her left eye. We could see all reason leave her face as we turned in slow motion for the door, leaving behind the noise of a woman who has had more than she can take.

I think the potatoes were the first to sail out of the open window into the garden, closely followed by the formation flight of the turkey with a sprout escort. In a matter of seconds it was all over. Mum had a triumphant swig from her wine glass. Outside in the blazing sunshine, our Christmas lunch lay in the shadow of the lemon tree. We looked slowly from one to the other, and the same unspoken thought crept warily into each of our heads. My brother, not wanting to make any sudden movements, edged towards the deep freeze. Gingerly he picked out a packet of sausages. Then, without a word, all four of us made our way to the beach.

Chris Tarrant

BROADCASTER

I absolutely love Christmas – I'm a sucker for all of it . . . Father Christmas, the reindeer, the carol singers coming round the house, the decorations, the mistletoe, the cards with snow scenes all over them (even though we haven't had a proper white Christmas in the south of England for at least a quarter of a century!)

I absolutely love it. Well, that is, with the possible exception of Christmas 1991!

I should have known that it wasn't going to be a tremendous success when, on Christmas Eve, reversing my car out of the Waitrose car park, I managed to do two hundred quid's worth of damage on a concrete post that I'm sure wasn't there when I drove in.

I also should have had a clue that it wasn't going to be the greatest Christmas ever when I managed to drop and shatter a bottle of Scotch, coming out of the off-licence.

I certainly should have got the general idea when I managed to reverse my Mercedes over my mother-in-law's Christmas cake, which I'd stupidly put behind the car as I ran into the house with the shopping, and then ran out again, forgetting all about the cake. Still, it was only Christmas Eve. Christmas Day could only be an improvement.

But little did I know, as 25 December dawned, that it was going to be even worse.

I did my usual Christmas morning live show on Capital Radio. I've done it every Christmas Day for the last nine years and funnily enough I really thoroughly enjoy it. For a start, I don't go on the air until 10 a.m., which is actually a lie-in for me compared to the rest of the year, so I unwrap the presents with my kids at breakfast time and then take a leisurely drive into the centre of London with absolutely no traffic on the road – it's probably the only day of the year that such a quiet journey is possible into the centre of town.

The atmosphere on the phones is great – people seem genuinely delighted and amazed that there's anybody there live on Christmas morning. Then I generally drive straight home in time for a large drink, and the turkey and, of course, all the cold cuts in the evening. At least that's how it's worked every other year! However, this particular year, I should have known it would be different. I don't know quite what I'd done in 1991 but I'd clearly upset somebody.

For starters, when I poured myself a very large glass of a particularly fine claret that I'd chosen the night before – from the same off-licence, incidentally, where I'd rather sheepishly had to go back for another bottle of whisky to replace the one that I'd stupidly dropped – it had a good colour, a good nose, and a good body, but unfortunately it was as flat as my mother-in-law's Christmas cake and tasted like vinegar. I couldn't even go back and harangue the owner of the off-licence, as he wouldn't be open again until Boxing night.

Anyway, things got back to normal. We found lots more wine that didn't taste like it would have been better sprinkled all over a bag of chips, the smells of roast turkey were wafting deliciously through the house and then came screams of horror from the girls in the kitchen. What now? I thought. Surely nothing else can go wrong. But it could and it had.

Ah – the joys of living in the country. It turned out that my wife, Ingrid, while waiting for the turkey to roast to perfection for a few extra minutes, had put the potatoes, sprouts and parsnips outside the back door to cool and, when one of the other girls went out to collect them, they were covered in what were unmistakably mouse droppings! In no more than fifteen minutes, in the middle of a bright winter's day, every rodent in Surrey seemed to have come out of nowhere and made a bee-line for all of our Christmas vegetables. At first we tried scraping them off but nobody really was very keen, and in the end we had a magnificent turkey with lots of stuffing, cranberry sauce and several tins of peas.

By early evening, having slept most of the afternoon, we were all feeling rather more than full of good cheer, had forgotten the disasters of the previous twenty-four hours, and the atmosphere was unmistakably festive. But then fate produced one final Yuletide arrow from his sling, just before the day was over.

As we sat back by the fire, drinking more wine, and licking our lips in anticipation of all the cold cuts from the enormous turkey that we'd only scratched the surface of with our tinned peas at lunch time, there was yet another scream from the kitchen.

In the hysteria that followed, it transpired that Bimbo, our incredibly stupid Golden Labrador, had also been slobbering in anticipation of cold turkey. In fact so much so that she had jumped up on the table, knocked the bird's carcass off and slobbered all over the remains. To say that Bimbo was *persona non grata* that Christmas would be an understatement. Bimbo was literally in the dog house until some time well into the New Year, and we spent Christmas night sitting pathetically watching a re-run of *The Poseidon Adventure* eating cheese on toast!

As I said, I love Christmas – well, most Christmases – but 1991 was ... Bah! Humbug!

Terry Wogan

BROADCASTER

A CHRISTMAS TALE

For the people who ran the small hotel, it was the busiest they'd been for ages. The manager, a sore-head at the best of times, whinged and bemoaned his lot. 'If it was raining soup, I'd have a fork!', he whined. 'We go for weeks with just the odd passing caravan, and here we are turning good paying customers away! I don't believe it!'

'There seems to be an awful lot of people on the move,' said the barman. 'God knows why.'

'You'd never hear anything in this God-forsaken little hole,' growled the manager. 'We're always last to get the news.'

'For goodness' sake, Josiah!' shouted the manager's wife. 'Can't you ever look on the bright side? The bedrooms are bursting, the bar's heaving, the restaurant is full! What more do you want? At least we're going to make enough money to see us through the New Year. Cheer up, misery-guts!'

Just then, there was a knock on the door. 'I'll get it,' said the manager, smarting at being spoken to like that in front of the staff. A man was at the door, and just behind him a woman on a donkey. 'Yes?' said the manager, testily.

'I wonder if we could have a room for the night, please. And perhaps a table for dinner?'

'Not another one,' muttered the manager, under his breath. 'Look, I'm terribly sorry, but we're absolutely chokker here, old boy, we haven't got room to breathe, never mind to let.'

A look of pain crossed the traveller's face.

'We've come an awful long way, and my wife is expecting any minute, and we can't find a room anywhere.'

'Look, mate,' interrupted the manager. 'Sorry for your trouble but I've heard a million sob stories like yours. There's no room, okay?' And he slammed the door in the traveller's face.

There were wild stories and rumours about a great, new bright star that shone over the little town that night, and how a woman had given birth in a disused stable with just some shepherds looking on, and how three richly dressed travellers had come to the stable with expensive gifts for the newly born baby, as if he was some kind of prince.

The manager and staff of the small hotel were too busy to notice, and *much* too busy to listen to ridiculous stories about stars, and stables and babies and kings. Business was wonderful, and the marvellous thing was, it continued to be wonderful, with a constant stream of visitors who had heard the rumours and were curious to see where the strange incident with the baby and the star and the mysterious travellers had taken place.

The little hotel prospered. So, too, did the manager and his wife. Some time later, she gave birth to their first, and only, son. They called him Barabbas.

The Beverley Sisters

SINGERS

MEMORIES OF CHRISTMAS

Once upon a time there were three little sisters, full of excitement, on the way to see their very first Christmas pantomime. They hadn't even *seen* a panto before, let alone one starring their own parents – The parents were Coran and Mills, superb concert-hall artistes, and the children were the Beverley Sisters.

We took our seats in the buzzing theatre, Joy sitting between the twins as usual (even in bed she slept in the middle). It was so thrilling for us just to be out at night at all. We had the most wonderful parents, but they simply had to leave us most nights to go out doing concerts to earn the rent, our bread and jam, and the nice pineapple chunks, each carefully counted from the tin, for our Sunday tea. How they hated to leave us at night but Joy was told to look after the twins as they were three years younger and she was even allowed to smack them (if absolutely necessary) but *not on the head*. They'd pester Joy to read aloud to them again and again. They'd wail, 'Read some more, or we'll tell Mum you hit us on the head!'

Back to the panto: curtain up – story gets under way – enter on stage our mother, the beautiful singing princess – we all gasp with joy – murky green lights then reveal the villain, the wicked uncle, our father. The whole audience hissed and booed – rendering the three of us mortified and inconsolable.

At the interval we rushed backstage to Dad, crying, 'Dad, Dad, it's horrible. They all hate you.' We've never forgotten his chuckle, as he said to us, 'Darlings, don't you see, that proves how good I am and how convincing I am as the villain, when I am really a comic. You should be proud of that.' We walked on air back to our seats and what a glorious second half we had, hissing and booing and cheering louder than the rest... Never ever dreaming that our lives would someday be spent up on that stage.

Leslie Crowther CBE

Harrod's is quite amazing, never more so than at Christmas time. The crowning glory is the Hall of Toys.

Sometimes, however, the peace is shattered. One year some bright spark in the presentation side of that particular department decided he would install an easel on which would stand a blackboard, with the requisite number of chalks, and an invitation to children who were in the toy department to write whatever they liked, particularly if it contained a request for a particular toy.

Well, we noticed several adults gathered round giggling more than somewhat, and on close reflection we saw exactly what they were giggling at. There in firm but childish handwriting was the opinion that Father Christmas liked looking at the pretty girls more than he liked talking to the children. We would have giggled along with the rest, but for the fact that the childish handwriting belonged to none other than Caroline Crowther!

Sir Cyril Smith MBE, LL D (Hon.), DL

POLITICIAN

Christmas for me has always been a happy time. A time for remembering and a time for giving, though it's nice to receive for it shows you have not been forgotten. I have often wondered, for example, whether I should send Christmas cards, but I do – I send about 600 – for so many of them are sent to people I have not seen for many years, or perhaps months. Invariably they send one back – and so 'we remember'. Mind you, I always try to buy cards that have some 'spin off' for charity! Wouldn't it be great if Royal Mail could be persuaded to give to the wonderful ChildLine, say 1p for every card posted in the UK – or even have two prices of stamps – one to give that penny, the other the normal charge for those not wishing to do so!

The first Christmas I can recall was when I was at primary school in my beloved Rochdale. Mum had little money, though we always had a long wool stocking hung up over the fireplace – filled with apples, oranges and other 'goodies'. My sister Eunice, my brother Norman and I would be up at the crack of dawn to see what Father Christmas had brought, what was in the stocking, and to make sure he had eaten the mince pie we had left. Happy days! My headteacher secretly brought me a present and left it with Mum for me.

I became a newsboy and we used to get Christmas tips. I saved so hard to buy my wonderful Mum the finest present I could afford. I was so proud. It was to be a pair of gloves. I arrived at the shop, only to discover I had lost the ten shillings purchase price. I just wept, I was so very disappointed. I was pleased in later years to buy her presents much more costly. I recall the joy on her face as she opened her surprises – and her tremendous joy when she gave me mine. Giving and receiving – the joy of Christmas. It's not the value, it's the thought.

In 1966 I was mayor of Rochdale. I visited on Christmas Day the local hospital's children's wards. I recall the joy of the children's faces. In the evening (and I did this for many years) I organized a concert of first-class entertainers for the homeless, in the local Salvation Army hostel. The men there loved it and it was a 'real good do'.

I held a party for deprived children – it was in Rochdale Town Hall. The hall keepers were worried about behaviour; they thought, I think, that the walls would be covered in jelly! They weren't for, you know, if you give children dignity and a cause for self-pride they normally respond accordingly!

I always attend my church in Rochdale on Christmas Day morning and conduct the service – as I will in 1995. That, too, is a pleasant and lively experience, meeting friends and sharing their experiences.

I look back, then, with happiness. I recall the parties, the food, the joy and the presents.

Sadly now, in 1995 as in 1994, my joy is tinged with sadness. I no longer have Mum. She died in March 1994 and I miss her terribly. I'll still have presents from my loving family and I'll give them too – but Christmas without Mum can never be the same. Parental love is a wonderful thing – those of us who have experienced it or still do, know that and treasure the experience. That is why I am pleased to make this contribution to try to help ChildLine – for so much of their work is with children who tragically do not always have that love and care.

May God bless them and the work of ChildLine.

The Rt. Hon. the Viscount Tonypandy PC, DCL

POLITICIAN

Once upon a Christmas Day when I was six years old (but nearly seven, because my birthday is in January), I lived in a home that had only one living room and two bedrooms.

Because our living room had a door leading out to the pavement, but no window at all for the two bedrooms, we always needed a candle to see our way around the bedroom.

My brother Ivor was a year younger than I was, and we always slept together. Eucrys, our big brother, was two and a half years older than me, so he slept at the bottom of the same bed. We used to have a lot of laughter as we cried out to Eucrys to take his feet out of our faces. We were young innocents, all devoted to our mam, who slept in the other bedroom.

On this special Christmas, Ivor and I had planned to stay awake to see Father Christmas when he came to fill our stockings, which we had hung behind Eucrys' head at the bottom of the bed.

Alas, sleep defeated us, and we did not see Father Christmas after all. When we woke at about 6.00 a.m., we crawled quietly down to the bottom of the bed to see if Father Christmas had come. We didn't mean to wake Eucrys, but when we discovered that our stockings were full with nuts and an orange and an apple we could not restrain our joy. We looked at each other in the dark and reached for the candlestick so that we could see better. We were chattering loudly and took no notice when Eucrys told us to go back to sleep. Oh, the sheer joy with which we tried to count the nuts!

After breakfast, which was inevitably early,

Ivor and I went out to compare with neighbouring children what Father Christmas had done for them. Next door to us lived a boy called Ivor Pippen, who seemed to have no mother. He lived with his father, who was accustomed to drink too much beer.

In great excitement I asked Ivor Pippen what he had had for Christmas and he showed me what was then a twopenny bar of Cadbury chocolate. I ran back in to my mam, nearly crying, as I said, 'Father Christmas only gave Ivor Pippen a bar of Cadbury chocolate.'

Mam looked at me in a strange way and said quietly, 'You know what to do, George.' I was puzzled, until she said, 'Share yours with him, George.'

Now when I am eighty-six years old (and nearly eighty-seven), I look back with loving nostalgia, thankful that I was in a loving house. Christmas is a time for giving, especially to children in need.

God bless Esther *and* ChildLine.

Ed Stewart

BROADCASTER

THE YEAR WAR ENDED

Christmas 1945 – the first one I remember. Being four and a half years old, my memories are a bit hazy, but two things have stood out in my mind ever since.

Being a war baby, recollections of the actual fighting in the Second World War are non-existent. There was no TV in those days and reporting and descriptions of events came through the wireless (as it was then called), newspapers and film newsreels. At the beginning of that year, though, I was playing in the garden with my cousin Ant (he was called that as short for Anthony; his mother, my aunt, called me Edward Earwig – strange that!) when we heard a whirring noise coming from the sky and, looking up, we saw zooming across the clouds a doodle-bug, one of the feared and very destructive German flying bombs. When the whirring stopped, the bomb would just drop – and you prayed it would be nowhere near you.

It was a rusty recollection of war – that, together with the shells of buildings, craters in the road, billowing black smoke and the horrible sirens. It was a Christmas which should have been a happy time and turned out to be one of the most horrid. My father had family who lived in Newfoundland and after the war was over and we were deep into food rationing, they sent us two huge parcels of food. Imagine the excitement that December when he carefully unpacked tins of pineapple and mandarin oranges, which we kids had never seen before, packets of jelly, bags of dried fruit and what to me were the most delicious of all, marshmallows.

My parents had been given a beautiful cut-glass serving bowl as a wedding present years earlier and into that Mother poured all those wonderful exotic, succulent and, most importantly, sweet fruits, together with some tins of condensed milk which had also been hidden in the food parcels. We were agog with expectation as pudding time arrived. We had kept chickens during the war, as many people had, and in return for a warm shed and endless pecking around for bits on the ground, those chickens provided us with fresh eggs and, on that first peace-time Christmas, made the final sacrifice and supplied us with a delicious roast meal.

As Mother carried the cut-glass bowl full of fruit, nuts, syrup and condensed milk into the dining room, disaster struck. My younger brother, still on all fours at that stage, managed to crawl straight into Mother's path. She went one way, the bowl went the other and thousands of pieces of fruit and splinters of glass covered the floor. After the cries and tears had subsided, we sat around waiting for the 'all clear'. That came when Father realized he hadn't opened the packets of marshmallows yet and, by the time we had gorged ourselves silly on those, we knew it hadn't been such a bad Christmas after all!

Now, every Christmas, my wife makes sure there are marshmallows on the table – and I can enjoy my sweet memories!

Toby Anstis

BROADCASTER

For me, it really was that magical night before Christmas!

As the next-door neighbours put the king on the cake and stuck the last balloon on the big chestnut tree outside the house, my twin sister Kate, Mum, Dad and I got dressed in our fancy-dress party costumes.

Then, after taking his last sip of hot wine and happily singing 'White Christmas', Dad Santa led his delighted female assistant and two elves out of the grotto.

It was a beautifully cold, crisp and festive evening. The sky was so clear that every star in the universe seemed to be shining on us!

What I didn't realize then was that I was later to see the biggest star of all, on his annual adventure of goodwill!

A stream of party-goers flowed into the house next door; on every person's face a huge smile; on their hands, thick woolly gloves; on their minds, well, just the inevitability of a smashing night out!

As the grown-ups chattered merrily to their friends, Kate and I and two other children crept upstairs to the landing! Awaiting us was a huge old wooden bay window, delicately laced with fairy lights and glistening white tinsel.

We told jokes we'd heard at school and complained about the big Christmas projects we'd been set over the holiday! When all of a sudden something caught our attention in the night sky!

A larger-than-normal star sped through the moonbeams, leaving a glittering wake. Before I had time to gasp, it had disappeared!

At that moment, the four of us were silent . . . we just looked at each other with disbelief!

'Was that . . . ?' whispered Kate anxiously. What seemed like just moments later, but was in fact more like an hour, our parents rounded us up, coats and gloves in hand, and we all left the party.

'The twins are unusually quiet,' muttered Mum to Dad. I looked at Kate, and we laughed behind our hands.

Fifteen or so years on, I still remember that evening vividly.

'Twas the night friends met up, chatted cheerily and ate good food.
But for four children, 'twas the night they saw the real magic of Christmas!
The night I saw Father Christmas!

Anne Charleston

ACTRESS

The only Christmas memory to which I can put a date occurred in the last year of the war, when I was four years old and desperately wanted a sleeping doll. Toys, particularly dolls, were in short supply, but by some means my mother acquired a porcelain doll's head of great beauty, to which was added, by courtesy of the Doll's Hospital, a stuffed cloth body, which included a crying mechanism, and celluloid arms and legs.

A family friend, who was a dressmaker, had cunningly stockpiled lengths of pre-war imported fabric, and my doll, Cecelia, arrived on Christmas morning dressed in a gown and bonnet of peach-coloured French chiffon, trimmed with cream lace, and ensconced in a beautiful, refurbished second-hand doll's bassinet.

She was the first proper doll I ever owned and she gave me years of pleasure. Her dark-brown eyes were fringed with thick black lashes and closed rather noisily when she lay down, and her rosebud mouth was permanently ajar.

Of course it was not until years afterwards that I understood all the love and effort that had gone into putting Cecelia together for me. I was allowed to believe that Santa had squeezed his bulk down our chimney and had personally deposited her at the end of my bed.

My other Christmases have, over a gap of so many years, merged into a happy blur, as the routine varied very little.

The day began at about five a.m., when I would wake up and begin attacking my presents with gusto. God help the rest of the household if they had had a festive Christmas Eve and wanted to sleep, because my excitement had to be shared!

The presents had to be temporarily abandoned at seven o'clock while we all got ready for mass. We set out at seven thirty as it was quite a long walk up the hill, and mass was at eight sharp.

I was never an enthusiastic mass-goer, but those Christmas mornings were different. There were always more candles, more flowers, more singing, and a beautifully arranged crib, complete with shepherds and a glittering star.

After mass, there would be morning tea with one or other of the neighbours and, as the morning marched closer to midday, the adults would open a couple of cold bottles of beer, which would be consumed in the shade of the verandah.

The traditional Christmas lunch of roast turkey and plum pudding studded with sixpences, or even shillings if Dad was feeling generous, was often eaten in temperatures of 100 degrees. But nothing would induce our mother to serve a cold lunch. Come Christmas, we observed the customs of our Irish forefathers.

When the table had been cleared and the dishes washed, we would all pile on to a tram and head for my grandparents' house, to meet up with the aunts and uncles and cousins. My grandparents had eight children, most of whom had married and had two or three of their own, so their quite large house would be heaving with sons, daughters, in-laws, and grandchildren of every shape and size, causing chaos as they exploded with the sheer joy of Christmas and family togetherness.

While the parents made futile efforts to calm us down, our grandparents smiled beamingly, and did nothing to curb our excitement.

I regarded my grandmother Bridie as my best friend. While most of the adults in the family required that children should be seen and not heard, she treated all her grandchildren with deep interest and respect and would spend hours talking to us, telling jokes and stories, and would even exchange opinions with us.

She was also a brilliant pianist and had in her youth aspired to the concert stage. So, at some point during the afternoon, the family would gather around the piano and raise their voices, while Bridie played Christmas carols, with lots of old Irish airs thrown in for good measure. Throughout all of this, my grandfather would sit back in his armchair, watching her with such love and pride, sipping on his twice-yearly glass of sherry (only Christmas and Paddy's Day).

Their house was only two blocks from the beach, so we children would all take our swimsuits and towels with us, and spend an hour or so splashing about in the sea, in grave danger of sinking, due to an excess of Christmas lunch. The mothers never swam but sat on the beach in their Christmas best, which included handbags, stockings and high heels, watching every move we made. How they expected to save us in a crisis is beyond me.

After that, still water-logged, we went back to the house for cold chicken, ham and salad, which consisted of sliced tomatoes, shredded lettuce and mayonnaise, the only type of salad known in Australia at that time.

The meal over, the Christmas tree became the focal point of the gathering, and the mountain of gifts surrounding it would be handed out one by one by Grandfather, a task he would surrender to nobody else, and rightly so, as with his thick white hair and drooping white moustache he was Santa to the life.

Australian Christmases have now, very sensibly I suppose, become much more casual affairs, with cold buffet lunches, or back-yard barbecues, but I still look back with nostalgia on those ludicrous traditional roast lunches, eaten in the blistering summer heat, the visits to my grandparents and the long rides home on the tram at ten o'clock at night, dozing over my large bag, filled with the day's spoils.

So many of that large, tribal Irish family have gone now. Bridie and Pa died within a few months of each other, when I was nine; all the parents have passed away and even some of the children from that far-off time. Those of us left have grown-up families of our own and we all celebrate our individual Christmases in different parts of the world.

Mollie Sugden

ACTRESS

A CHRISTMAS BOAT

William was six years old. He lived in a fisherman's cottage on the very edge of the quay, where lots of small boats were moored.

All his friends at school regularly went out on the boats, as their fathers were fishermen. But William's father was a postman, and William had never been on a boat. One day he asked his father, 'When will you buy a boat?' His father laughed and said, 'When we win the lottery!'

Every day William looked out of his bedroom window at the boats, bobbing up and down, with their masts swaying. There was one boat that he liked more than the rest. It wasn't a fishing boat, it was a small pleasure yacht. White-painted with blue trim, it was called *Sending Cloud*. Oh, thought William, if only he could go sailing on that boat. But the owner rarely came to use his boat, and when he did board her, he was extremely grumpy. Once William asked his mother why the man was so grumpy, and mother explained that not long ago the grumpy man had a little daughter about the same age as William, but he had lost her when she and her mother were in an accident, and now he was very lonely.

On Christmas morning William had woken very early and excitedly examined the contents of the bulging stocking which had appeared miraculously during the night. At seven o'clock, his mother called, 'William, breakfast time.' For once William was already dressed and was just about to run downstairs when something outside the window caught his eye. He stopped. Was he seeing things? Could it be? There on the deck of *Sending Cloud* stood a man in a red cloak and hood, a man with white whiskers. He was looking up at William's window and beckoning.

William rushed downstairs to find his father and mother smiling. 'Yes,' they said. 'Santa Claus is out on *Sending Cloud*. We must put on warm coats and go out quickly.'

In a daze William found himself going in a dinghy and being helped aboard by Father Christmas. He noticed immediately that the twinkling eyes of Santa Claus were remarkably like those of the grumpy man!

'Come aboard,' said Santa, 'and come below.' Below was a neat warm cabin and, in one corner, a small Christmas tree. Hanging from the tree was one card labelled 'William'. Mother read it out to him: 'Every weekend, when the weather is calm enough, William is expected to board the *Sending Cloud* and put out to sea for a jolly day out.' William looked at his father and stammered, 'But, how –?' His father said, 'I expect a little seagull told him.'

William was so delighted that he hardly remembered going back home. But he distinctly remembered the grumpy man joining them for Christmas dinner, and games and fun during the rest of the day.

As William went up to bed that night he looked out of the window at the harbour lights reflected in the water, and he knew two things for certain. The grumpy man was not grumpy at all. And William had had the best Christmas in the world.

Helen Shapiro

SINGER

Being Jewish, we didn't celebrate Christmas, but I was always aware of a certain atmosphere at that time of year. I would envy my Gentile friends the fact that they had Christmas trees and decorations in their homes, and would moan to Mum and Dad about it a lot.

However, as a concession to the seasonal festivities and to the fact that Christmas generally falls at a similar time of year to the Jewish festival of Chanukah, presents were exchanged. When I say exchanged I mean that my brother Ronald and I would be given a little something which Dad would place at the end of our beds during the night (Santa Shapiro!). It wouldn't be much because there was never any money around, but how thrilled I was to wake up and find some new little game or, most often, a book. I loved books.

One thing I did get to do each Christmas was help put up paper-chain decorations in the school halls and classrooms and I was always involved in the school concert or play, usually either singing or narrating. I remember one particular Christmas concert in which not only did I narrate but, along with a friend of mine, gave a highly spirited, if somewhat ungainly, demonstration of the rock'n'roll dancing known as jiving, which had just exploded on to the music scene via Bill Hailey and the Comets. That was 1955. I hasten to add that I'd only just turned nine!

One of my favourite events at Christmas time was being taken, along with lots of cousins, to see the famous lights in Oxford Street and Regent Street. What a magical time that was for a young child. We would get our first glimpse of the lights from the top of the bus (probably the No. 73 from Stoke Newington) and then we would walk. There was for me an almost tangible feel about the place at that time of year, and

31

how I loved it. We would have tea at Lyons Corner House at Marble Arch, and would then be taken home to dream of all the wondrous things we'd seen.

The religious side of Christmas was, of course, lost on me. After all I was brought up not to believe in Jesus. However, in 1987, I came to the realization and belief through studying the Bible (Old and New Testaments) that Jesus (I also like to use his original Hebrew name, Yeshua) was and is all he claimed to be: the promised Messiah of Israel and saviour of mankind; and that this belief was not inconsistent with my Jewishness, contrary to popular myth.

Interestingly enough, I still don't celebrate Christmas because its origins aren't Biblical but pagan and it's more of a commercial exercise than anything else. I actually celebrate Messiah Jesus every day and connect him with Passover and other Biblical feasts rather than with Christmas.

Having said that, there's still something about that atmosphere at Christmas time that I've never lost from my childhood. It's something to do with that wide-eyed innocent wonder which we lose as adults but which sometimes, just sometimes, manages to shine through a little crack in the mundane everydayness of life. I hope I never lose it altogether. Merry Christmas.

Carol Smillie

BROADCASTER

CHRISTMAS MEMORY

Christmas will always be a very special time for me, a time of new beginnings, old friends, and happy endings. I was even named Carol because I was born at Christmas, so that makes it extra special for me! If I had to think about the *best* Christmas, I know exactly which one it would be . . .

I was seven years old and my mum and dad had been telling me it was time for bed for ages, but I was far too excited to sleep. Tomorrow would be Christmas Day and I had been on my best behaviour for weeks! I'd done the dishes, finished my homework and even kept my bombsite of a room tidy, but I knew it would all be worth it: after all, Santa had been keeping an eye on me, and he must have got my letter.

Dear Santa,
My mum and dad have told me if I'm very good and wish very hard, you'll bring me 'Pokey Peke', so please can I have a 'Pokey Peke'?
  Love Carol x

Now, I know what you're thinking. What on earth is a 'Pokey Peke'? You can forget the Power Rangers or Barbie. When I was seven years old Pokey Peke was a little battery-operated Pekinese dog. He barked, he jumped, he did somersaults and was your best friend. Was there anything he couldn't do? I don't think so.

Eventually I ran out of excuses for staying up so late, so I left out the cocoa and biscuits for Santa and was packed off to bed by my two older sisters, even though my big brother Jim wasn't even home yet (it's *never* fair being the youngest!).

I lay still for ages, hoping they'd believe I was fast asleep, and when it had all gone quiet, I crept up to the window to see if I could see Santa coming. As I rested my chin on the window ledge, I could feel the cold air on my face.

Outside, it was like a fairy tale: everything was covered in a perfect, glittery, magical white blanket of snow, and I imagined that if I sneezed, it would all blow away! I began writing my name in the condensation on the glass and didn't notice at first, but gradually the lights in the distance were coming nearer. I looked at the clock and realized it was already twelve thirty, and this was my brother only just coming home! I jumped back into bed before anyone came upstairs with him but it seemed ages before that happened – there was some kind of commotion going on in the kitchen downstairs. I was desperate to find out what, but I must have fallen asleep eventually, dreaming of the next day …

I awoke with butterflies in my tummy and ran downstairs to waken everyone. 'For goodness sake, Carol, it's six a.m.,' groaned Mum. After lots of persuasion, I managed to drag the whole family out of bed. (It's a tradition in our house that everyone has to be up before the presents are opened.)

The hall looked different somehow, overcrowded. The furniture from the lounge had been pushed out. Wow! I thought. There must be *so* many presents inside, there is no room for the furniture!

When I crept round the lounge door, there in the middle of the room was a beautiful, brightly coloured Wendy house. I shrieked with delight and my brother and sisters urged me to go inside amid lots of knowing looks and giggles. As I pulled back the red cloth door there was a little shoe box inside, a shoe box with strange noises coming from inside. 'Go on!' they all chanted. So I lifted off the lid and a little wet nose came out, then a little pink tongue licked my hand, and I could hardly believe my eyes for there was no 'Pokey Peke' but, instead, the real thing. She was an adorable little black mongrel. What a Christmas!

I found out later that Trudy (as we named her) had been abandoned at a few days old, and my brother and his friend had found her and brought her back to our house. My Mum wasn't too keen to have a real dog, but couldn't resist those big brown eyes! They hatched a plan to keep her out of my way until Christmas Day when they would surprise me!

Trudy stayed with us for sixteen years until she died, a very happy, loved and cared-for old lady. And for me, it was the best Christmas ever!

Alan Titchmarsh

BROADCASTER AND GARDENER

A YORKSHIRE CHRISTMAS

'But I don't *feel* Christmassy,' I would complain to my mother right up to the twenty-something of December. 'You will. There's plenty of time,' she would reply. And by 24 December I always did. Between the ages of about six and ten, Christmas would seem to be wasted if it wasn't looked forward to with feverish excitement. Pleasant anticipation was not enough.

In our back-to-back terrace house in Ilkley, Yorkshire, during the fifties and early sixties, the weeks leading up to Christmas were full of landmarks for my sister and me. The first of these would be the cellar being declared out of bounds. This happened sometime in November. I never knew why. Was there, I wondered, some kind of deal being struck with Father Christmas? The coal was kept in the cellar and Father Christmas came down the chimney – but other than that the two things seemed unconnected. My plumber father would spend his evenings down there, accompanied by the sound of sawing and hammering, and the smell of new paint would waft into the front room from under the cellar door. It was a mystery. The cellar was whitewashed, so what was he painting? But I never went down there.

There was the Christmas cake to bake in November, too, so that it could have a chance to produce its full flavour by the time the festive season dawned. No silver threepenny bits went into ours for fear that Auntie Alice or Grandma would lose a tooth, but we all had to take the wooden spoon out of Mum's hand and give the clarty mixture a stir and make a wish before it went into the grey enamel gas oven, seemingly for hours, to fill the house with its warm, rich aroma. This, I thought, must be the scent of frankincense.

I was a choirboy – and a bellringer, too, when I grew large enough to reach the ropes – and during the weeks leading up to Christmas I sang every single carol at least half a dozen times at services and choir practices. I learned never to sing the last verse of 'O Come, All Ye Faithful' until Christmas Day, and that only the ladies sang the first 'O come, let us adore him' in the chorus bit. I knew that in 'The Holly and the Ivy' there was an odd line where you had to sing 'the-e playing of the merry or – gansweet singing in the choir', even though it sounded daft. Who or what was 'gansweet'? And what did the 'merry or' play? But one year I was a star. The first verse of 'Once in Royal', trilled in a raw treble from the back of the parish church at the carol service, was my moment of fame, before we processed to the choir stalls in purple cassocks and crisp white surplices, with starched ruffs that gave every choirboy a red ring around his neck by the end of the service. By their next laundering at Easter they would be floppy again, but right now they were as sharp as sandpaper.

Uncle George, at 6 ft 2 in, would bellow in a deep bass from the choir stall opposite, and my father's 5 ft 8 in high tenor would ring out behind me as I swanked among the high notes and showed off my E above top C.

Back home, on the corner of Nelson Road, by the bus garage, there would be desultory conversations with the other kids in the street about who was getting what from Father Christmas. One lad in particular always seemed to have a brand new bike, or flashy roller-skates, or a Scalextric set in a big box – the sort that had two chicanes. It never struck me that Father Christmas was uneven in his distribution of goodies when the bike I got was second-hand. I put it down to the fact that the lad's parents were both heavy smokers and that Father Christmas was somehow connected with Kensitas gift coupons. My mother muttered something about 'the never-never', which I took to be a reference to *Peter Pan* at the Bradford Alhambra. We'd been to see it. Alastair Sim played Captain Hook, with prominent red veins on his white stockings.

On the two evenings immediately before Christmas there was a chance to really get into the Christmas spirit with carol singing door to door, rather than from the choir stalls. Those members of the choir who were up to it would meet at the church at around six o'clock – hopefully with a fair distribution of tenors, basses, trebles and altos – and then wander up the posh end of town, delivering a better class of carol to those parishioners in detached houses who were kind enough to leave their front doors open in spite of a biting wind whipping off the moor, and who were generous enough to put something crisp rather than chinking into the collection box.

This was in the days before our obsession with charitable causes. The spoils would be divided up and shared among us – it was a seasonable perk that seemed fair recompense for turning out twice each Sunday throughout the year and on all those interminable Sundays of Trinity, which now they call Pentecost.

We'd finish off, each year, at one of the largest houses in town, right at the top of Grove Road. The door would be opened by Mr B., the portly master of the house who was something big in wool, and who would invite us into the galleried hall. The lady of the house would welcome us and usher us into the vast and opulent drawing room. The church organist would take his seat at the grand piano and we'd perform our grand finale before being treated to sausage rolls, sandwiches and drinks – Bristol Cream sherry for the grown-ups and Kia-Ora orange squash for us nippers.

Mrs B. discovered that I was interested in art, though how I can't remember, and took me out into the hall for a tour of the oil paintings that stretched right up the ballustraded staircase. 'This is my son when young,' she said, pointing at a large oil painting of a youth in a pale-blue shirt, casually reclining against a tree. 'I told the painter that I would always know it was my son because of his hands.' I felt sad that she clearly didn't think much of the face. Then, with Christmas greetings shouted from the grand doorstep, we snaked our way down the tree-lined drive and drifted off in different directions to our homes.

On Christmas Eve my dad would come home from work late, his flat cap at a rather more rakish angle than usual and his normally pallid and whiskery cheeks flushed pink. The tweed jacket over his navy-blue bib-and-brace overalls would be bulging and he'd sidle past my mother and open the stair door, cocking

37

his head in my direction to indicate that I should follow him. On the landing he'd push his hand inside his jacket and pull out a paper bag, reaching inside it for my mother's present. One year it was a leather-cased manicure set. What did I think? Would it be all right? Would she like it? It was the first time I ever remember my father asking my opinion about anything, and I remember being proud that he wanted my reassurance, and touched by his love for my mother. He was a gentle Yorkshireman who rarely expressed his feelings, but I'll never forget those moments of conspiratorial kindness underneath the large brass plate that hung on the wall at the top of our stairs.

With my seal of approval noted he'd slip my mother's present back into its paper bag and, somehow, have it wrapped in Christmas paper by the following morning. My sister and I would sit at the bottom of their double bed and I would watch him look at my mother as she opened it. If she were really pleased she'd cry and we'd all look away.

But that was after Christmas Eve, the most difficult night of the year as far as sleep was concerned. My sister and I would leave paper sacks at the foot of our beds and read ''Twas the Night Before Christmas' to one another. Then the lights were turned out with a severe instruction to '*Sleep!*', and we tossed and we turned and eventually we slept.

'Has he been?' we'd bellow in the morning, but by then my toes would have felt the difference in that once-limp paper sack which was now stuffed at least half full with goodness knows what. I remember one Christmas morning being silently disappointed that there wasn't much in it, and then discovering that Father Christmas had brought me an electric train set which he'd had to leave downstairs because the vast lump of chipboard on which the loop of track was nailed would not go into the paper sack. It was the same year that he brought me a book which contained a cardboard toy theatre with characters and scenes from *Aladdin*. It cost one shilling and sixpence, said the label on the corner and, to my father's dismay, I played with it all day, having run the train around the track a couple of times and parked it in the siding.

The electric train was my last big present before I 'grew up'. In the years before that came the garage – white, with blue knobs to open the front doors that revealed two Dinky toys – and the zoo – red and yellow with real wire cages and sliding doors to allow the animals in – and a grey fort with castellated battlements and a real drawbridge that lowered on a hinge of chamois leather. They were all beautifully hand crafted, and they all smelled of new paint. I don't remember what happened to them, but I still have a fat zoo keeper made of lead. And my mother still has her manicure set.

Edwina Currie MP

I wasn't brought up to celebrate Christmas; my family were Orthodox Jews and quite strict. We children did get presents, and there were lights and much jollity, but it was usually a couple of weeks earlier, for Chanukah. That is a festival of rededication, so in a way I was well imbued with the wonder of rebirth – of welcoming something new and precious – even though I wasn't too sure exactly whose birthday was being celebrated on 25 December.

However, Jewish people in many countries will help out at Christmas in order to give other people the day off. Often their time is spent in hospitals, when they discover a secret – that a very merry time is had by all, including staff who often come specially for the events.

There's no greater spectacle than a distinguished surgeon carving an enormous turkey on a platter in the middle of his ward, surrounded by patients suitably dealt with in previous days, many of them weak with laughter at his cavorting, laughter which any doctor would admit is the best medicine. I suspect that food safety laws probably make such demonstrations of surgical skill less common than they used to be, but I'd like to meet the hospital manager who would try to put a stop to it.

So let me confess a secret: I love singing carols (my father would turn in his grave) and may occasionally be found in our local general hospital on Christmas Eve with the nurses as they do the last round of the night. In Derby, where Florence Nightingale was a local girl, there's something specially magical about the nurses, their cloaks drawn around them, white caps on heads, each equipped with an old-fashioned lantern, as they walk down darkened corridors into hushed wards, singing softly as they go. I defy you to hear 'Silent Night' under these conditions and not be moved to tears of gratitude and wonder.

The first year I went, I was surprised to find several wards, mainly surgical, almost full. I asked the doctor, 'Surely you try to get people home for Christmas?' He looked a little embarrassed. 'Not these patients,' he whispered. 'They're the ones with no family. They'd be alone at Christmas. So we ask if they'd mind terribly coming in for their operations in the week before, and point out that they'd have to stay just about to New Year. They always accept, and we make sure they enjoy themselves.'

And, he failed to point out, they get the best Christmas present – a new hip, or knee joint, or relief from the problems of pain and discomfort which had troubled them, and fresh hope that all will now be well.

One year, however, I wondered quite what was going on. As I stood with the choir and did my bit on 'O Come, All Ye Faithful', I suddenly felt something creeping up my leg. To my horror it felt like a hand, and it was exploring rather thoroughly.

I looked down. It was indeed a hand and it appeared to be attached to a young man in the bed, who was strung up with drips, tubes and attachments; the only free part of him was his wandering digits.

'Hello!' he croaked hoarsely. 'Mrs Currie? I thought it was you.'

He was one of my Young Conservatives.

'Good Lord!' I said. 'What are you doing here?'

He groaned. 'Got appendicitis. Emergency op at two this morning. I'm stuck here for the duration.' The hand reached out again but I seized it quickly in mine and patted it as I commiserated.

There was a youngster, typically energetic and casual as so many of his generation are, who, thank goodness, never needed ChildLine, nor any professional help until this disaster struck him. As I left I remarked to him that perhaps now, having seen our Health Service at first hand, he might appreciate it and defend it in future. He nodded and tried to smile reassuringly. I certainly will, and do.

George Melly

SINGER AND WRITER

The great occasion of the year at Chatham Street was the family party held towards the end of the week after Christmas. Almost every Melly and Smith living was present and, in the case of married women, *née* Melly, their husbands and children also. The one notable exception was Willie Bert's mother, Great-Aunt Beatrice, who lived in southern England. After a toast to 'absent friends', Willie Bert always leapt to his feet and proposed 'My Mother' as a codicil. It was more likely her geographical rather than her 'invidious position' as a divorced woman which prevented her presence at the Chatty parties. Not that distance alone kept many members of the family away. My Great-Aunt Nell and her daughter Cousin Nell were assiduous attenders. They both lived together in London in an Edwardian mansion block off the Fulham Road with eau-de-Nil walls and fine Dutch furniture, but stayed a great deal at Chatham Street and indeed lived there during the Hitler war; Aunt Nell looking after Uncle Bill, Cousin Nell driving a Civil Defence ambulance throughout the Blitz. Aunt Nell and her daughter were known as 'Old Nell' and 'Young Nell'.

Old Nell was, I suppose, plain but with so glowing and saint-like a personality that she seemed to be beautiful. Like Aunt Eva she made no concessions to current fashion but her dresses, while black and floor length, were Edwardian rather than Victorian, and she always wore a tight, boned neck choker in the manner of Queen Alexandra. Unlike Eva and Florence, whose philanthropy was severely practical and objective, Nell's faith insisted on a St Francis-like involvement with those she tried to help. She was preyed on by many petty con-men who came to her with optimistic schemes for self-improvement, and when in London she would visit the embankment night after night with food and money for the down-and-outs. Aunt Eva found this approach intensely irritating, referring rather contemptuously to 'Nell's lame ducks'.

It was at the Chatty party that the remaining Riverslea Mellys surfaced: Cousins Leonard and Fanny, both old and as poor as church mice. Leonard's dinner jacket was green with age. Rotund, bustling Fanny gave us children only half-a-crown each but they were always mint half-crowns which she had drawn especially from the bank.

It was this huge and noisy party then, three generations of them, who assembled yearly for the great family feast. What happened at it was as fixed and immutable as a religious ceremony.

Before dinner the rarely used drawing-room was opened up although the chandelier remained in its shroud. Sherry was on offer. The meal was huge, even by Chatham Street standards. The youngest member of the family had to propose a toast, an obligation which made my sister Andrée almost ill with nerves when it came to her turn. Toasts completed, a long and very boring event followed. The senior member of the family recited this catch to the person on his or her right:

> Do you know the muffin man, the muffin man, the muffin man?
> Oh, do you known the muffin man who lives in Drury Lane?

To which the person so questioned replied:

> Oh, yes, I know the muffin man, the muffin man, the muffin man,
> Oh, yes, I know the muffin man who lives in Drury Lane.

Then both parties would intone together:

> Then we *two* know the muffin man, the muffin man, the muffin man,
> We *two* know the muffin man who lives in Drury Lane.

Then the person to have answered the question first turned towards whoever was on his or her right and repeated it; was answered in the affirmative and the three acquaintances of the muffin man agreed in unison that they knew him too. Unbelievably, this rigmarole continued until everybody at the table – there must have been well over thirty most years – could shout out the final chorus:

Then we *all* know the muffin man, the muffin man, the muffin man,
We *all* know the muffin man who lives in Drury Lane.

Some tried to enliven this incredibly tiresome chore by putting on funny accents but most, with surprising good spirits, simply played it straight. It was never suggested that it might be curtailed or dropped altogether. That would have been considered almost blasphemous.

After everybody agreed that they knew the unnaturally gregarious muffin man, the ladies went into the library and the gentlemen drank port or brandy and told mildly indecent jokes. Boys were allowed to remain in the dining-room from about the age of twelve for this initiation into masculine mores. Even Uncle Bill became quite animated and told a story about the sexual habits of the Kaiser. He also usually described a 'feller' he had seen on the stage in Paris in the early 1900s who could fart several tunes and blow out a candle at a considerable distance by the same means. Nobody really believed this, but quite recently it was revealed as fact and a book on the gentleman, 'Le Pétomane', was published proving that Uncle Bill was telling the truth.

The men, whether laughing at the Kaiser's inadequacy or pretending to believe in the exploits of 'Le Pétomane', all wore dinner jackets and, the same year that I was allowed to remain behind with them in the dining-room, I wore one too. This was not new – the idea of spending money on a dinner jacket for a growing child would have appalled my father – but had been handed down for several generations. Even so I was extremely pleased with myself, despite Tom's joke at my expense earlier in the evening. I'd gone into his dressing-room, ostensibly so that he could tie my bow, in fact to solicit admiration, but all he'd said was, 'Don't annoy the little man. They're very touchy, these dwarfs!'

I must have looked rather hurt because he immediately explained the source of this mysterious but unflattering reaction. As a small child in Sefton Park he had seen a dwarf out walking with his 'owner', a showman attached to a travelling fair then *in situ*. He had scampered curiously towards it, to be met by this informative reproach. Once I'd understood it was only a joke I was completely mollified. I even repeated it on arrival.

When we left the dining-room to 'join the ladies', it was discovered that my brother Bill, jealous that my three years, seniority allowed me to stay on, had concealed himself under the table. He told me later that he had understood nothing that had been said and had grown extremely bored. In fact my own reaction had been more or less the same, but of course I wasn't letting on. 'You will when you're older,' I assured him dismissively.

The final stage of the Chatty party took place in the library. It was in two parts: 'The Great Divide' and the entertainment. 'The Great Divide' was the name given to the doling out of money in lieu of presents, a rational if somewhat impersonal solution to the problem of how to reward so large a gathering. Uncle Bill would slump in his accustomed chair, Davis would carry in a silver tray piled high with brown envelopes like wage packets. She would stand by her employer and he would pick up the envelopes at random, reading out the name written on each of them: 'Young Nell', 'Gillian Leather', 'Samuel Heywood Melly'. Each of us in turn would go forward, collect our envelope, and kiss him on his cold indifferent cheek. Each knew exactly what to expect: £50 for his generation, £25 for my father's, £10 for those in their twenties, £1 for my contemporaries. It was rather a soulless exercise, the only excitement arising from the order in which we were called and the possibility, never fulfilled, that someone might have been accidentally left out.

The entertainment followed immediately. Gangie and Gampa would offer one of 'Mrs Caudle's Curtain Lectures'; we would perform a carefully rehearsed sketch; others played the piano or recited comic monologues. One year, during Aunt Eva's lifetime, a Rawdon Smith girl – I believe it was Hope, one of Willie Bert's daughters – tap-danced to a gramophone record, having first changed into shorts. Aunt Eva was visibly put out at this immodesty which must have upset Willie Bert. He was always extremely solicitous towards the old ladies of the family.

As Uncle Bill had already suffered his stroke before I was old enough to attend the Chatty parties, he had relinquished his bird-watching and photography and in consequence no longer 'prepared and showed his magic-lantern slides as part of the entertainment'. I gather that this was no great loss. Young Nell once told me that the performance lasted a long time and that the slides themselves were so blurred and indistinct that the whole enterprise had become known to the more irreverent members of the family as 'Owls in a Fog'.

During the war the Chatty parties became smaller and one year, during the height of the Blitz, there was none at all. Uncle Bill died in 1944 after several days in a coma. Davis, who had looked after him with extreme devotion, told my mother, with initial reluctance, of his end. He had regained consciousness on a cold but bright winter's evening and hauled himself up in his narrow bed to face the setting sun. 'Oh hell!' he'd muttered resignedly and fallen back, dead.

The Rt. Hon.
Sir David Steel KBE MP

POLITICIAN

MY FAVOURITE CHRISTMAS MEMORY

More years ago than I care to remember, I decided to take my young family to Kenya for Christmas. I spent four of my happiest boyhood years there, and was looking forward to arriving in time for the Christmas Eve watchnight service at St Andrew's Church, Nairobi. My father had been the minister there in the 1950s and he had organized the construction of the church.

Unhappily, we were trapped by fog at Heathrow airport – along with thousands of other passengers – for about twenty-four hours. As a result, we actually saw Christmas in on the overnight flight. Judy, my wife, had knitted beautiful Christmas stockings for each child to hang up for Santa Claus when we arrived in Nairobi. Instead, to the amused delight of the other passengers, she hung them on the back of the seats in front of us. When the two youngsters awoke, there were the stockings, bulging with Santa's goodies. Just how Santa and his reindeer managed to come down the chimney into the aeroplane will forever remain a mystery, as we were all sound asleep, of course!

Anthea Turner

BROADCASTER

We have always made a big thing of Christmas in our household. It was our mum, really. She never had any brothers or sisters, and she always felt she had missed out and, as we all know, other people's Christmas presents are always more interesting than our own!

My earliest recollection of Christmas was being told to leave a mince pie and a glass of Ribena for Santa Claus. When I woke up the next morning, there were crumbs where I had left the mince pie, an empty Ribena glass and a footprint on the window sill. This was because I had already questioned how Santa Claus was going to get down our chimney as Mum and Dad had just had an electric fire fitted!

With the arrival of my two sisters, Christmas became more exciting. But sadly at the age of five I suggested to my two-and-a-half-year-old sister Ruth, much to the annoyance of my parents, that perhaps Santa Claus didn't exist. Determined to stay awake and find out the truth, I had seen my father creep into the bedroom late at night with sackfuls of presents.

But this didn't dampen our spirits. Being a little theatrical, plays were always on the agenda. The three of us and our dog Pat, who played a sheep, a donkey and a camel, managed to perform the Nativity for our parents who must have had handkerchiefs in their mouths trying not to laugh at the seriousness of the whole event. The Baby Jesus was played by my, now, thirty-five-year-old teddy bear, Brian. Maybe we were ahead of ourselves with *The Life of Brian*!

Another highlight of the Christmas festivities was 'What will Nana be wearing?' Her love of clothes makes me look like an amateur. But her eccentric and flamboyant style knew no bounds. She could look glamorous wearing a table cloth and, I kid you not, she often did –

appliquéed with roses and anything else which fell off the Christmas tree. In all the years I knew her, I never saw her without a hat and on Christmas Day you would think Ascot had come early.

Moving forward to my teenage years, Christmas became more 'How can I persuade my mum and dad to buy me the latest fashion trend?' Christmas 1974 I discovered make-up! Auntie Jean bought me every teenager's dream – a complete Mary Quant slap kit. My only problem was, I thought you had to wear it all at the same time! It was unfortunate that this was also the year Dad invested in a ciné camera. Maxis were in and I entered shot looking like a reject from the *Addams Family*.

Fortunately I married a man whose family equally feels that Christmas is a great celebration and I can't see the tradition ever dying or losing its shine in our household!

Michael Aspel

BROADCASTER

CHRISTMAS – HOME AND AWAY

The very first Christmas I can remember was when I was two years and eleven months old. On 23 December, my father crept into my bedroom in our London flat and whispered, 'Come and see what Father Christmas has brought us.' He carried me into my parents' room, and there was a tiny, red-faced creature waving its arms about and making squeaking sounds. This was my present, a baby brother called Alan. I had been hoping for a set of building bricks, but I tried not to show my disappointment. The last Christmas we had together, before the Second World War came along and forced us apart, was when Alan was four and I was seven. This time my presents included a metal box of paints. Alan took a fancy to them and we had a bit of a struggle. He wanted to close the box, I wanted it open. He won. I still have the scar across my thumb where the lid slammed shut.

When the war came, we were evacuated from London to Somerset, out of the way of the German bombers. Alan and our elder sister, Pat, were sent to live with one family, and I went to another. We were away from London for more than four years. The local school had a bright idea for our first Christmas away from home. They collected a huge pile of toys and put them in the assembly hall. There were dolls, train sets, cowboy suits and games galore.

Then we all sat facing these goodies, each of us wondering which one would be ours. Our names were picked out of a hat, and we were allowed to choose whatever we wanted from the pile. For some reason I can't remember what Alan and I got. What I do remember is that our sister Pat's name was the last to come out of the hat. By the time she went up, every doll and game and outfit had been taken. All that was left was a little glass-fronted box with balls in it that you rolled into holes. I recall her brave smile. One Christmas, an exciting-looking parcel appeared at the cottage. My foster-mother hid it away until the big day and, although I searched high and low, I didn't see it again until Christmas morning. It seemed to rattle rather a lot, and when I tore off the wrapping I realized why. The parcel contained a set of model aircraft, made of lead, I think, and they were all broken. I was devastated. But help was at hand. My foster-father worked at a local foundry, and he took the wreckage of the planes and welded the bits together. They looked a bit weird, with big lumps half-way along the wings, but it was better than nothing.

The greatest Christmas of all was, of course, our first back home in London. Our small flat was bursting, as all our aunties and uncles and cousins joined us for a wild party. There were balloons and bottles of all shapes and sizes, there was music and dancing and non-stop laughter. I was in charge of putting on the records and changing the needles on our old radiogram. My last memory of that evening was of my Uncle Arthur insisting that he had to walk to Brighton, which was more than fifty miles away. Actually he only lived around the corner. People laughed so much, it became his party-piece, and he has said it at the end of every Christmas party ever since.

Sue Lawley

BROADCASTER

Once upon a Christmas we lost our dog. She's a Golden Retriever called Cleo. She's twelve years old now but I think what happened to her nine years ago had a profound effect on both her and us.

It was our first Christmas in a new house. We had bought it full of enthusiasm and hope, knowing that we would find the energy to restore it to its full Victorian glory. But you know how it is: as the preparations for Christmas grew ever more frenetic, our energy levels began to fail and the prospect of our first Christmas in the home we had dreamed of grew a little daunting. We determined on one last rally. Summoning up our draining strength, we bought a Christmas tree, hung the decorations, moved the furniture around a bit and invited the neighbours in for a Christmas Eve drink. It was going to be a jolly festive season after all.

The neighbours were due at lunch time. During the course of the morning my mother, Peggy, nipped down to the shops to buy some more icing sugar for the mince pies. Cleo's exercise having been somewhat neglected in the general pandemonium, she took the dog with her. She came back half an hour later with the icing sugar but no dog. While walking along the parade of shops she'd almost been the victim of a nasty accident. A motorist, perhaps because she was finding Christmas as stressful a time of year as we were, accidentally threw her car into reverse, mounted the pavement and knocked over a tall pile of metal bread crates before smashing into the plate-glass window of the bakery. Shattered glass flew everywhere and the crates spilled along the pavement, banging into people, cars, lampposts and doorways. It was bedlam and the noise was explosive. Cleo took fright. An extremely well-behaved dog, she never went to the shops on a lead but trotted quietly at heel. Not on this occasion. Terrified, she turned tail and bolted.

To begin with, we thought she'd find her way home. But she didn't. By the time the first neighbours were sipping their mulled wine, we were still one short in the household. Distracted, I would offer them a friendly nut or crisp before dashing to the front door to see if Cleo was back. There was no sign of her. In the end, I left the party and toured the streets, leaning out of my car window calling her name. She was nowhere to be seen.

A worried gloom enveloped us. The neighbours, sensing tragedy, went home early. We rang our nearest police station in Putney. They dutifully recorded our loss but had no information with which to comfort us. They told us not to ring other police stations in the area. At the headquarters their computer network would be able to tell us if Cleo had been found. As darkness fell, we realized we might never see her again.

It was one of the saddest Christmas Eves I can remember. My daughter Harriet, then six years old, curled up in Cleo's basket and said that was where she wanted to spend the night. She was only persuaded into her own bed on condition she could leave a note beside the mince pie and glass of sherry in the fireplace. 'Dear Santa,' it read. 'All I want for Christmas is Cleo back.'

But Santa didn't bring Cleo back that night. Another call to the police confirmed our fears that she must have spent a cold night alone on the common. It was impossible to be cheerful. Nobody wanted turkey. Even opening presents had a desultory air about it, with frequent pauses to wonder where Cleo was, who might have her, or even whether she was alive. Before a second dusk fell on her absence, we put on our coats and walked the neighbourhood looking and calling. Nothing.

On Boxing Day we'd given up all hope of seeing her again. In one last desperate act, I decided to ignore the advice of Putney police and ring every police station I could think of in the neighbourhood. I picked up the phone and dialled Barnes.

'I'm looking for a golden retriever,' I said. 'I don't suppose you can help me.'

'Is she a nice gold colour and makes a lot of noise?'

'I think so,' I said, my heart doing a double somersault.

'I wish you'd come and take her away,' he said. 'She's been here since Christmas Eve.'

I don't think I said anything else. Throwing the phone down, I yelled to the family and we dashed to the car. Within minutes we were outside the police station, where the station sergeant took us to the underground car park. 'Cleo!' we called into the cavernous darkness and a familiar barking came from behind a small half-door where she'd spent the Christmas of 1986.

She covered us in licks and we covered her in tears and kisses. The sergeant said, 'I was going to ask you for proof of identity but I don't think I need to.' For us, Christmas could now begin.

I said at the beginning that this was an experience which had a profound effect on both Cleo and us. We've hardly let her out of our sight since then, even though these days she's old and unlikely to go far. As for Cleo, any sudden noise sends her scuttling away. The clang of a saucepan, the bang of a door or the heavy drumming of a bus or lorry makes her recoil in anxiety. For us that Christmas is just a vivid memory. For Cleo, it's given her an instinctive reaction to alarming sounds that's been part of her make-up ever since.

Prue Leith OBE

COOK, WRITER AND BUSINESSWOMAN

A family Christmas may be wonderful but it is also a nightmare. Indeed, in my family we have an expression, 'feeling Christmassy', which means feeling frazzled, short-tempered and probably tearful.

There is good reason for this. Even in childhood Christmas wasn't an unremitting blessing. I'm ashamed to say that my first display of the family Christmas spirit was when I was eight and could not control my sulks on receiving a pillowslip full of *books* when I was dreaming of a pony, or at the very least a bicycle. (For some reason we did not hang up stockings, we put pillowslips at the end of the bed, and woke up to our main presents. How I expected a horse or a bike to fit in a pillowcase I don't know, but my conclusions were correct – my father's long and unsuccessful campaign to get me to *read* had begun. Incidentally, every Christmas Eve I'd attach my pillowcase by string to my toe so that as Father Christmas filled it I'd be able to wake up and remonstrate with him if he'd not listened properly. Of course, I never woke up.)

Other yuletide events reinforce the memory of the family Christmas spirit. My first attempt at cooking was a Christmas cake, made in Domestic Science and carried home proudly. I'd iced it with smooth white icing and painted a picture of the three kings on top of it. But I'd omitted to put any glycerine in the icing and it set like concrete. Parental pride turned first to amusement and then to fury as my father, unable to cut the thing, called for a hammer and hammered his thumb and then proceeded to split my mother's favourite bone-handled knife by using it as a chisel. We ended up turning the offending object over and scooping the cake out of the solid icing bowl. It's a wonder I became a cook at all.

My professional memories of Christmas aren't too good either. As a young freelance cook I once spent the week before Christmas cooking for the grandees who ran the Cordon Bleu School at Winkfield Place in the Berkshire countryside. Every afternoon I had to send up a sponge cake to the drawing room. Every afternoon a critique would come down with the butler. 'Too heavy – not enough eggs', 'Too damp – you undercooked it', 'Too dry – you overcooked it', 'Pockets of flour in the mix – you under-folded it', 'Too solid – you over-folded it', 'Too bland – you forgot the vanilla'. You would not believe how many things can go wrong with a simple sponge cake. Finally I knew I'd got it right. It was the most perfect sponge cake you ever saw. The message came back, 'Good cake. Pity you didn't peel the paper off the bottom'.

Still, that Christmas was memorable for two other reasons, both good ones. I was given Christmas Eve and Christmas Day off, and was to spend them with friends in Surrey. This was the early sixties and there were still public baths at Victoria Station. Since hot water wasn't a reliable feature of my digs at Winkfield, I paid 1/6d for an enormous white towel, a bar of Wright's Coal Tar soap, and a huge bath of wonderful hot water, run by a white-uniformed attendant. As I lay soaking in the sublime hot water gazing at the cubicle's functional white tiles through the murk of thick steam, I listened to carol singers below, competing on the station concourse with train announcements and guards' whistles, and the attendant's cheerful 'Happy Christmas' and 'Oh thank you, Madam' as contented, warm and clean customers left the baths. A surreal experience.

My other memory is equally romantic, and is of the same evening. I boarded the train with an arm-load of mistletoe gathered at Winkfield and, since the compartment was crowded, I put the mistletoe in the luggage rack above me. In the British manner, Christmas Eve or no Christmas Eve, no one exchanged a word. But when the young man opposite me got up to get out at his station, he suddenly said, 'I can't resist it', and bent and kissed me on the cheek, and scuttled out. He left the ice so broken that the rest of us had a very jolly journey full of seasonal cheer. Today he'd probably be arrested!

Since I've been properly grown-up, with a career and children of my own, my experiences have been equally mixed. Once, listening to the radio, I caught the tail-end of a 'Chef's Tips' programme and heard some expert saying that if you deep-fried chestnuts, they would pop easily out of their skins and save your fingernails and temper. What I had not heard was his careful instructions to split the skins right round with a knife first so that they *could* pop off. I duly lowered a kilo of chestnuts into the hot chip-fat. The chestnut flesh cooked and swelled, and the tough skins resisted, until, baff, they were exploding like hand-grenades all over the kitchen and flinging up fountains of boiling fat. I grabbed the nearest thing to a blanket, which happened to be my husband's best wool coat, and, hiding under it like a criminal on the way to court, crept up to the pan to turn off the gas. I now buy peeled chestnuts in tins.

In my years as a cookery writer I got thoroughly fed up with Christmas, because it had to take place in July to catch the Christmas magazines. There is something disheartening about decorating a tree, and cooking turkey and plum pud in the heat of summer. One year I had to assemble all the children I could to be in the 'happy family' picture, and they were as good as gold as their legs scorched in front of the blazing log fire and their arms ached as they posed holding stacks of heavy plates, the pudding or the turkey. The photographer was the slowest in England and was driving my eighty-year-old mother mad because he *would* not push the button when he'd managed to get us all smiling, but delayed and delayed until smiles had frozen and tempers worn thin. It took all day, and we couldn't even eat any of the dinner at the end of it because it had all been out in the heat of summer, supplemented by the heat of the fire and that of the camera lights all day – a real recipe for food poisoning. I had just binned the last of it, and undecorated the window sills and the tree, when the message came that the photographer had left an empty roll of film and a roll of camera tape in the middle of the Christmas table, clearly visible in every single photograph. We had to stage the whole shoot again, with a borrowed family, mine having wisely gone on strike.

But some of my memories are as sentimental and wonderful as 'Jingle Bells'. Memories of the children staging a nativity play and the real live donkey eating Baby Jesus' cradle. Or the same donkey cantering off with a seven-year-old Mary on his back when they were supposed to be leading the carol singers. We have a video of a family production when, as my son solemnly reads 'A star is born', a great hairy grown-up arm appears from behind the curtain holding aloft a silver paper star. One December, when the children were full of the Three Kings and their crowns, an upholsterer called Mr King arrived at the door to quote for some curtains. My daughter, looking into the back of his van and seeing a gold lampshade, came hurtling into the house, yelling, 'I've seen the King's crown, I've seen his crown.'

So I can't agree with Noël Coward's 'Why don't we cancel Christmas? Let's pack the whole thing in'. However ghastly the telly commercials are, however 'Christmassy' we all become, every year I end up doing, and loving, the lot – carols, tree, trips to the panto and that time-honoured annual gastronomic blow-out.

Since I think that cranberry sauce and bread sauce are what *really* make that turkey delicious, here are foolproof recipes for both – and one for brandy butter too!

CRANBERRY AND ORANGE SAUCE

SERVES 8
Juice of 2 oranges
225 g (8 oz) sugar
450 g (1 lb) cranberries

1. Put the orange juice and sugar together in a saucepan. Allow the sugar to dissolve over a gentle heat.
2. Add the cranberries and simmer very slowly until just tender.
3. Serve cold.

BREAD SAUCE

SERVES 8

1 large onion, peeled
12 cloves
570 ml (1 pint) milk
2 bay leaves
10 peppercorns, or 1 pinch of white pepper
pinch of nutmeg
salt
110 g (4 oz) fresh white breadcrumbs
110 g (4 oz) butter
60 ml (4 tbsp) cream (optional)

1. Cut the onion in half. Stick the cloves into the onion pieces and put with the milk and bay leaves into a saucepan.
2. Add the peppercorns, nutmeg, and a good pinch of salt. Leave to stand for 30 minutes, then bring it to the boil very slowly.
3. Take the milk from the heat and strain it on to the breadcrumbs. Add the butter and cream. Mix and return to the saucepan.
4. Reheat the sauce carefully without boiling.
5. If it has become too thick, beat in more hot milk. It should be creamy.

BRANDY BUTTER

225 g (8 oz) unsalted butter
225 g (8 oz) caster sugar
grated rind of 1 orange
60 ml (4 tbsp) brandy

1. Cream the unsalted butter and sugar together until very light.
2. Add the orange rind and brandy to flavour strongly. Serve well chilled.

The Rt. Hon. Virginia Bottomley MP

POLITICIAN

CHIMANIMANI

It is difficult to know with growing and grown-up children how long they will continue to be with us for Christmas.

A few years ago we took all three to the Mozambique border of Zimbabwe to stay with the Plunkets, old friends who have lived for decades at Rathmore, by the Chimanimani Mountains.

We hired a car from Harare which had travelled a distance equivalent to a one-way trip to the moon and its tyres were no longer ready to give trouble-free journeys to a large family.

One puncture on the first day and four more during the week were reminders of the reliability of motoring nowadays in the United Kingdom. Once the tread of a tyre wheeled past us. We appreciated the assistance given willingly by other travellers and locals. During the longest stop, two of us helped in a local school whilst waiting for a repair.

Robin and Jennifer Plunket are remarkable hosts. They have lived under the threat of terrorism during some of the years of UDI while working for reconciliation and full democracy.

The wildlife has echoes of the Garden of Eden. Walking in the hills was healthy and reading by gaslight provided echoes of home entertainment lost in these days of television and videos.

On Christmas Day we attended the local church with hymns and carols augmented by cassettes of a cathedral choir recorded in England.

Perhaps we should try to spend one Christmas each decade in another continent to remember that Jesus was born neither in England nor to a family in comfortable surroundings.

Our family Christmas visit to Africa should be a constant reminder of each child throughout the world. The joy or the sadness of every child means as much to their parents wherever they are.

Paul Daniels

Every year, I get asked by journalists, 'What is your earliest memory of Christmas?' and, every year, the story is the same.

I was born in 1938 and very shortly afterwards, war broke out. This meant very quickly a complete disruption of normal family life. At that time, my mother and father and myself were living at 10 Lower Oxford Street, South Bank, near Middlesbrough. South Bank seems to have been built in order to house masses of people to work in the docks or the steel works that surrounded us. Long rows of terraced houses, with two rooms upstairs and two rooms downstairs, were the order of the day and the toilet was outside, at the end of the back yard.

My mother was getting fatter, which I know now meant that she was going to have a baby. When the baby arrived, on 23 December, two days before Christmas, my father, who was in the Royal Navy, was given compassionate leave to come home and visit us, which of course was wonderful for me. By then, the bed had been moved down into the front room and Mom had given birth to my brother Trevor at home, which was quite common in those days. Also, probably for reasons of finance as well as space, the baby slept in a drawer pulled out of a dresser. Like everybody else of my age, I was wondering what Father Christmas would bring me and, very early on this war-time Christmas morning, I crept down the stairs and into the lounge where Mom, Dad and the baby were sleeping soundly. Amazingly, Father Christmas had filled my stocking and there were gifts strewn around the floor but pride of place was taken by a metal toy machine-gun on a tripod that stood just waiting for my tiny hands to grasp the two handles on the back end. In wonder, I grabbed them both and squeezed what turned out to be the triggers and this toy gave forth a loud rat-tat-tat-tat-tat noise and, at the same time, sparks shot out of the muzzle. In amazement, I hung on to the handles, making the noise go on seemingly for ever. You have to remember, this was war time so my dad automatically dived under the bed, the baby woke up screaming, my mother woke up screaming and I think by then I was yelling as well. Of course, it then went on to be what I have had ever since, a great family Christmas surrounded by not only family, but also good friends.

Every year now, when I watch my sons, nephews and nieces opening their presents, I travel back in time into that tiny front room and when I say watching them 'triggers' off a memory, you'll know exactly what I mean.

Janet Brown

ENTERTAINER

When I look back to my childhood days, I think to myself, 'Was I a greedy little girl at Christmas, or just an optimist?' Whatever, when it came to hanging up my stocking from the mantelpiece, it was my navy-blue gym knickers that went up instead, with a great big safety-pin holding each elastic leg together, so that my presents would not fall through! Yes, on second thoughts, I'm sure I must have been an optimist.

There is a song in *The Sound of Music* called 'A Few of My Favourite Things', and 'brown paper parcels, tied up with string' was certainly one of my favourite things. You can keep your fancy wrapping paper with its reindeer and holly! To run through to the kitchen early on Christmas morning and see that large brown paper parcel peeping over the waistband of my knickers was joy indeed.

Imagination does wonderful things. Leading up to that magical Christmas morning, I would sit for ages looking out of the kitchen window. There was a large hut at the top of the garden with a big window, I think it was probably a storage shed. Anyway as far as I was concerned it was Santa's workshop. I knew he was in there busy making toys. For goodness sake, *I could see him*! A shadowy figure, I grant you, but he was definitely there.

Another brown paper parcel that caused great excitement was one that arrived from America every year. It was from Aunt Teen. We – when I say we, I mean I, my brother and sister –

well, we had never met this aunt, but every Christmas, regular as clockwork, our parcel would arrive. What a lovely feeling the unwrapping of a parcel is, especially with the glamorous word America attached to it. We all knew that there were dollars inside. My father said they were worth quite a lot, which of course was great news for us. It meant we could do our shopping and choose our own gift.

My memories of a childhood Christmas would not be complete without telling you about the famous Clootie Dumpling. Clootie is the old Scottish word for cloth. Don't ask me the recipe, I never knew it. I was told, 'Oh, it's just a wee bit of this and a handful of that', and then the chance to lick the wooden spoon when the bowl was cleaned out. The result? A magic moment which my mother achieved every year.

I can see it now, being brought in on a large plate, put down in front of the fire, where it sat steaming, shiny and plump with sultanas. But the taste of it. Never since have I tasted anything so good.

I've had all kinds of Christmases since then. Some in my own home with my family, some with friends. The years may have added a colouring of their own, but nothing has ever been quite like the joy and magic of those childhood days. A happy, happy Christmas memory.

Gary Rhodes

BROADCASTER AND CHEF

EVERYBODY'S 'CLASSIC' CHRISTMAS

It's now Christmas Eve. There's still a lot of Christmas shopping to be done, as well as finishing decorating the Christmas cake, rolling out the pastry for the mince pies and stuffing the turkey!

We set out early to finish the shopping, thinking of course that we'll have it all done and sorted by 2 or 3 o'clock in the afternoon.

The shops are packed, you can't find what you are looking for, and if you can they don't have it in the right size! You finally finish your shopping and it's time to go home. However, the time is now 6 p.m. The presents are put to one side – remember, the children are still up. The turkey gets stuffed, the mince pies made, it's 10 p.m. and the Christmas cake is now going to get the mock snow effect!

Well, that's taken an hour. It's 11 p.m., time to wrap the presents. You had lost track of just how many there are – loads!

So the wrapping finishes at 2 a.m., and it's Christmas Day, and time for a quick drink before bed.

Next, you are being pulled about by the children saying Father Christmas has been and left a stocking full of presents. The clock tells you it's 6.30 a.m. – aargh! Anyway, it is Christmas. The children look so excited and happy so it's time to get up.

Downstairs Santa has also left a stack of presents under the tree. The opening process begins. It's great fun to watch the children's faces; you really don't mind getting up early after all.

Time for breakfast and a nice cup of tea. By now it's 9 a.m., time to start cooking, remember we have guests arriving at 11.30–12. Lunch needs to be served between 1.30 and 2.00 p.m.

The turkey and the pork go in. The carrots are peeled, parsnips ready for roasting, sprouts for boiling, to say nothing of chipolatas, bacon, bread sauce, extra stuffing, cranberry sauce and gravy! And that's just the main course!

It really makes me exhausted and full just thinking about it. Of course, because we are entertaining we are having a starter – prawn cocktail, pâté, smoked salmon, something like that.

The guests arrive late and we sit down at 2.30 p.m. By the time we've eaten a starter and that huge main course and the Christmas pudding arrives, there's only room for, 'No, no, just half that slice, thank you.'

We've had a couple of bottles of wine; we're absolutely full. Time for a quick sit down before clearing up.

What happens next? We fall asleep and wake up at nearly 8 o'clock, we've missed James Bond, still not cleared up and certainly haven't got any room for the cold turkey, pork, beef and ham salad!

So Christmas Day finishes with a pot of tea and half a dozen Quality Street!

It's funny, Christmas is so stressful, the fridge is packed with far too much food and that bowl of nuts and odd-shaped box of dates never do get eaten!

Will we change it next year? I doubt it. One thing we should do every Christmas is think of the children – *all of them*.

Happy Christmas!

Albert Roux

CHEF

BOUDIN BLANC DE VOLAILLE TRUFFÉ

SERVES 18 AS AN HORS D'OEUVRE,
OR 9 AS A MAIN COURSE.

4 slices white bread
125 ml milk
5 shallots
50 g butter
200 g chicken breast fillets, well chilled
200 g pork back fat, derinded and well chilled
5 eggs, well chilled
500 ml double cream, well chilled
75 ml port, preferably white
12 g cornflour
20 g fine salt
100 g truffles, finely chopped (optional)
50 g slightly stale fine brioche crumbs, sifted
2.5 m pork sausage casing
1 lt milk
50 g coarse salt
150 g butter, melted and cooled
6 leaves of gelatine (optional)

1. Remove the crusts and cut the bread into cubes. In a saucepan, bring the milk to the boil, add the bread and stir with a spatula. Immediately, take the pan off the heat and leave for 30 minutes at room temperature until cold. Rub the mixture through a fine sieve and refrigerate.

2. Peel, chop very finely and sweat the shallots gently in the butter for 2 minutes. Keep in a cool place.

3. For the stuffing, cut the chicken breasts and pork back fat into large cubes, mince finely in a food processor and rub through a fine sieve into a bowl set in crushed ice. Break the eggs into another bowl and beat lightly with a fork as though you were making an omelette, then mix in the cream. Using a wooden spatula, gently fold this mixture into the meats, working continuously until the stuffing is smooth and homogeneous. Still using the spatula, work in the bread and milk mix.

4. Mix together the port, cornflour, shallots and fine salt and stir it all into the stuffing mixture. Finally stir in the truffles, if you are using them, then the brioche crumbs.

5. To fill the boudins, using a funnel and your thumb, or a sausage filler, push the stuffing into the sausage casing. Tie a knot in the casing or tie it with string every 10–12 cm. Make about 18 sausages in this way. Prick each one in 4 or 5 places with a needle.

6. To poach the boudins, place them in a large shallow pan, then pour in the milk and 3 litres water and add the coarse salt. Set over a high heat and heat to 80–90°C. Do not let the temperature rise above 90°C or the boudins may burst. Lay a cloth over the boudins to keep them immersed and to ensure that they cook evenly, and poach for 18 minutes. Leave to cool completely in the cooking liquid. At this stage, you can keep the boudins in the fridge for several days before cooking them further; if so, when you take the pan off the heat, add 6 leaves of gelatine to the poaching liquid. Transfer the cooled boudins to a large bowl, pour over the liquid and leave in the fridge until needed.

7. To cook the boudins, make a light incision down their length and peel off the skin. Roll the boudins in the cooled melted butter and cook gently in a frying pan or under the grill for 4–5 minutes, turning them over after 2 minutes. They should be pale golden all over. Serve very hot.

Barry Cryer

BROADCASTER AND WRITER

It was Christmas over thirty-five years ago. I was in hospital. I'd been down in London, from Leeds, for three or four years, but nobody knew I was an in-patient, as I'd been admitted rather suddenly.

I resigned myself to the fact that I would have no visitors. Easier said than done. On Christmas Day, the ward was full of families and friends. I alternated between reading and pretending to sleep. It was during one of those fraudulent periods of slumber that I became aware of people round my bed. I opened my eyes.

The King family were assembled with presents. The three King brothers, a top musical act of the day, had become friends of mine, but it was still a shock. They stayed, we laughed and talked and then they left.

I didn't care about Boxing Day – I was ahead of the game – they had made my Christmas. On Boxing Day, they came again. 'We just happened to be in the area.' A severe attack of choking on my part. You wait ages for a wise man and then three turn up all at once. You don't wait for the Kings – they turn up.

Lesley Garrett

SINGER

When I was a little girl, my two younger sisters and I lived on the bend of a river that had been cut off at each end of the loop to form an oxbow lake. Every year, two swans nested on this lake. Just after Christmas, when I was nine, my sisters and I went for a walk and, to our horror, discovered our two swans frozen into the ice. The winters in Yorkshire when I was a child always seemed to be hard and bright, and the sight of our swans stiff and lifeless in the crystal-clear sunshine filled us with dismay. Even worse, one of them had been attacked by a fox and the ice was covered in blood. The other one was nearer to the shore and I could just, by holding my sister's hand on the bank and reaching out, touch it and felt that it was still warm. We were all very excited as we thought it might be still alive. I dispatched my sisters back to the house for a wheelbarrow and, in the meantime, using a big stick, started trying to hack my beloved swan out of the ice. By the time my sisters got back we were, between us, just able to drag it to the bank. It was enormous and we were very tiny. It must have weighed three or four stone and it took all our puny effort and strength to lift this huge bird on to the wheelbarrow. Then, cold and wet and trying hard not to let the swan's head drag along the ground, we took it home to our incredulous parents, who even to this day have a vivid memory of their three little girls pushing a wheelbarrow containing an enormous swan into the living room and shouting, 'Daddy, Daddy, build up the fire. We have to save the swan!'

Our parents were wonderful. They saw immediately that the swan was dead but they didn't want to hurt us so they wrapped it in blankets and rubbed its feet and tried very hard to bring it back to life and then, very gently, explained that it was too late but that we were very brave girls to have tried to save it. We buried the swan in our garden, which took quite a lot of effort on my father's part as the ground was frozen and hard. But he did it all the same and we said prayers and sang Christmas carols and gave the swan a real Yorkshire send-off.

We were very sad for a long time afterwards but the next spring two more swans arrived on our lake. We liked to think that they were the children of the first pair, and they continued to nest there for many years.

Simon Brett

MY FIRST JOB

It's very strange, a lot of people don't believe in Father Christmas. But I know he's real. You see, I once was Father Christmas.

It was my first job. I'd just finished at university and I'd applied for some serious, long-term jobs, but I needed something to bring in a bit of money for a few months. So I went down to what would now be the Job Centre, but then was called the Labour Exchange, and I asked if they had any temporary work going.

'Well,' said the woman, 'the local department store is looking for extra staff over the Christmas period. In fact,' she went on, 'I think they're looking for a Father Christmas.'

And that's how it happened. I've still got the card which I had to take to the toy department. It said: 'This introduces Mr S. A. L. Brett for the advertised vacancy of – Father Christmas.'

In the toy department I met the woman in charge, and she asked me to do a couple of 'Ho-ho-hos' to see if I was up to the job. Well, I must have passed the audition because she said yes, you start work tomorrow. The ladies in the ladies' alterations department ran me up a very nice Santa suit in fluffy red material and, at the age of just twenty-two, I was master of my own grotto.

Now I know I wasn't the real Father Christmas. I know I didn't spend my days supervising elves in the manufacture of toys, and I know I didn't spend Christmas Eve zipping round the sky in a reindeer-pulled sledge, dropping off goodies down everyone's chimneys. (Mind you, if I had been the real one, I would have found out the answer to a question that's always puzzled me: how does Father Christmas deliver presents to households that don't have chimneys? Does he somehow get in through the central heating pipes?)

I'm pretty sure all the children who came to see me in my grotto knew I wasn't the real Father Christmas. For a start, I looked pretty young for the job. Then again, as a lot of the tinies who pulled it off realized, my beard wasn't real.

And, even if they hadn't been made suspicious by those little giveaways, the presents I gave the children would have left them in no doubt that I was only a pretend Father Christmas. Or, if I was real, I was a jolly mean and inefficient Father Christmas.

You see, all these kids would come in, and I would say to them, 'Ho-ho-ho, and what do *you* want for Christmas?'

And the girls'd say, perhaps, 'I'd like a pony', and the boys'd say something like, 'Ooh, I'd like one of those remote-control Porsches that goes vroom-vroom-vroom all over the floor.' And, whatever it was they asked for, I'd still say, 'Well, that's very interesting', and hand over some horrid little plastic ball made in Korea.

Honestly, I felt bad about that while I was doing it. These poor little kids, their mums and dads'd told them that Father Christmas would answer all their wishes, and they ended up with a really cheap bit of tacky rubbish. I wonder, has anyone ever known a department store Father Christmas give a present that was worth having?

By the way, if you're ever offered the great career opportunity that I was, don't rush into it. Being Father Christmas is not all fun, let me tell you. For a start, it's seasonal. However well you've done the job, come Christmas Eve you're out on your ear. Also, it's very hot. That suit that ladies' alterations ran up for me may have looked good, but it felt like I was wrapped up in cotton wool. And then there was the beard, and the hat, and the big belt, and the gumboots. It was like living in a microwave.

But even worse than all that, there was the music. The department store had one tape of Christmas songs, and they played it

74

continuously. Now that was fine for the average shopper, who came in for ten or twenty minutes to buy something, but if you were stuck in a grotto for seven weeks, it had a terrible effect on your brain.

The memory of that tape's still with me, you know, and I don't think I'll ever escape its influence. I mean, last Christmas I went to one of my children's carol concerts. Everyone there was singing away cheerfully on 'Hark, the Herald Angels Sing!', and at the end there was silence, except for one solitary voice – mine – which went straight into the start of 'Rudolph, the Red-nosed Reindeer'. That had been the next song on the department store tape, you see.

So, if you're ever asked if you want the job of Father Christmas, think twice before you accept it, all right?

The Rt. Hon. Tony Blair MP

LEADER OF THE OPPOSITION

My earliest Christmas memory goes way back to when I was four years old. The memory is very vague, but I cannot have been much older because this was one of the Christmases that I spent in Australia while my father was lecturing at the University of Adelaide. The traditional image of Christmas, with its snow-covered rooftops and Santa Claus dressed in a large red coat, must have made little sense to me while I sweltered in the heat!

As a child, like most children, I was excited at the prospect of receiving presents. Unfortunately, at this age, the true meaning of Christmas was still a little beyond me. I expect that the concept of presents was something new to me that year. Each childhood Christmas I would focus on one particular present that I hoped to receive more than anything else. One year it was a tennis racket, and when I was a little older I wanted a bike. As I became more interested in music I would anticipate the arrival of a new record to add to my collection, the Beatles being an early favourite.

I always woke early on Christmas mornings, hoping to find a pile of presents waiting for me. Whether I got exactly what I wanted I don't recall, but I expect colouring pencils and sweets were among the presents, and there would always be at least one book from my education-conscious parents.

My childhood Christmases were very enjoyable times for me. The memories of my final Christmas in Australia stand out because my family's return to England meant that there would be no more Christmas afternoon walks down to the beach where we could eat ice-cream, and the only use for the gift of an umbrella would be to keep the rain off your head rather than the baking hot sun. Christmas in

County Durham would be no less enjoyable and the scenery no less beautiful, but it was certainly different.

I was very fortunate to have a loving family around me as I grew up. I realize that many children do not have this advantage; nor, in many cases, do they have an acceptable standard of living. For them, Christmas becomes just another reminder of what other people enjoy and what they have to go without. While other children are looking forward to spending time with their families and giving and receiving presents, those children who have to go without these joys of Christmas may feel unloved and unwanted. Without ChildLine they would have no one to turn to. ChildLine provides this essential service not just at Christmas but every day of the year; and for ten years they have provided invaluable help for countless thousands of children. It is a great pleasure to be asked to contribute to this book. I wish ChildLine a very happy tenth anniversary and all the very best for the future.

Lord Habgood

FORMER ARCHBISHOP OF YORK

A CHILDHOOD CHRISTMAS

My mother had a very generous nature and tended to overdo things a bit. Tea parties, for instance, were lavish affairs with never fewer than three different kinds of cake, not to mention sandwiches and scones, most of which remained uneaten. She was lavish, too, in giving presents, and at Christmas she used to excel herself. One of my earliest memories is of going round our town with presents for all and sundry. Nor were her children left out. On Christmas Eve we hung up pillowcases at the end of our beds rather than stockings, and in the morning they were duly filled with unlikely objects from Woolworths. For years I kept a nose flute which had mysteriously appeared in this way. It was a disgusting object, especially when played by several people in succession.

But the greatest evidence of lavishness at Christmas time was the fact that Father Christmas came twice – once on Christmas Eve, and once at teatime on Christmas Day.

It used to happen like this. My father, who was a country doctor, was invariably called out to see a patient in the middle of Christmas tea. Not long after he had gone we would hear the faint ringing of a bell at the end of the garden, and would crowd to the dining-room window to see what it was. I can still recall with a shiver the sight of a red-cloaked, white-bearded figure walking slowly across the lawn with a sack over his shoulder. At the front door he exchanged a muffled greeting in a slightly familiar voice, deposited the sack, and hobbled off into the darkness. I always felt sorry for my father for missing this high point of the year.

I have vivid memories too of huge parties for Christmas lunch. As a small boy I was teased by my elder brother who pretended to hold races between cheese mites along the dining-room table. A suspicion of blue cheeses lasted for many years afterwards, and I still sometimes look to see if I can spot anything moving in a very ripe cheese.

Memories of young childhood are particularly intense around Christmas, and I count myself extremely lucky that they are all happy ones. The 1930s seem a very innocent period in comparison with the 1990s. We made our own entertainments as a family; nobody drank too much; we enjoyed each other's company; and though what we did was lavish, it was not selfish. My parents were much involved in the life of the town, and the Father Christmas who called on us so memorably called too at the local Infant Welfare Centre in which they were both leading figures.

In later years, when I was a priest and then a bishop, Christmas was for me a working day. This has its own delights, not least in trying to make Christmas worship a memorable experience for others. But when one has spent the morning administering communion to many hundreds of people, there is a lot to be said for taking the rest of the day quietly.

Richard Stilgoe

ENTERTAINER AND WRITER

THE NIGHT BEFORE CHRISTMAS

'Twas the night before Christmas, and all through the flat
Not a creature was stirring – not even a rat.
The light had gone off on the silent TV
(We'd seen *Back to the Future*, *Jaws III* and *ET*)
I'd had three Peperami, a litre of Fanta
And now I was ready and waiting for Santa.
I knew he was coming – I knew I was right
For Mummy and Daddy had kissed me goodnight
And Mum had said, 'That noise – I heard it again, dear.'
To which Dad replied – 'No, it's only the rain, dear.'
I tried to ignore my digestion's loud rattle
(For three Peperami put up quite a battle).
And that's when I heard them – the sleighbells a-jingling,
The shouted instructions that set my scalp tingling –
'Come Rudolf, come Lynford, come Gunnell, keep prancing –
Come Carling, come Gower, come Gascoigne, come dancing.
Come Heseltine, Fergie and Beatrice, don't slack –
Portillo and Lilley, keep up at the back!'
I heard their hooves clatter and scrabble for grip
(For our roof is quite steep and it's easy to slip).
I heard Santa alight and I heard my heart beating
For then I remembered – we have central heating!
The flue-pipe is tiny – he hasn't a hope
But surely he's magic – of course – he can cope.
He'll squeeze down the chimney – he has – that's the noise

80

Of a very small man with a sack of small toys.
He's got to the boiler – I heard a small cough –
Poor Santa – I hope that the gas is turned off.
Go back, Santa Claus – it's not too late to jump.
Oh, no! I can hear him – he's caught in the pump.
He's off on the circuit, through all of the rads –
The hall, then Sam's bedroom and then Mum and Dad's.
He's going through mine now – I heard a small clank!
It's the towel rail next, then the hot water tank.
Then back to the boiler – now, gasping for breath –
He can't have survived. What a horrible death.
Hush, listen! – Exactly, there isn't a sound –
Poor Father Christmas has definitely drowned.
How shocking! No stockings, no gifts any more
No presents for me, or for Kevin next door.
The kids of the world will be simply appalled
And blame us, for having the heating installed.
My brain in a fury, I had a small weep
And, pale and confused, must have fallen asleep.
I woke to the sound of the pipe's early knocking
Remembered the horrors, then noticed my stocking.
The varicose sides and the end-of-toe tumour
Betoken the Rolos, the Twix, the satsuma!
I cried 'Santa lives – it was only a dream!'
(The heating cheered too with a small hiss of steam!)
What a nightmare – but my fault. I must have been barmy,
Last thing at night to eat three Peperami.

Lord Ashley of Stoke

POLITICIAN

A CHRISTMAS STORY

It was Christmas Eve and Jack and Stan were going to a party. Or so they thought. They were very excited, and as they were both the same age as Jennifer they knew she would have six candles on her birthday cake.

'It's not a good time to have a birthday,' said Stan gloomily.

'Oh yes it is,' said Jack. 'Any time's a good time for a birthday because you get presents and a party, and all that.'

Stan shook his head. He often did that and he worried about lots of things. 'It's a bad time,' he said. 'She will get her presents mixed up with Christmas presents and she won't know which is which.'

'Never mind,' said Jack. 'So long as she gets the presents, it doesn't matter.' But he didn't know what was going to happen.

'It does matter,' said Stan. 'If Father Christmas sees her birthday presents, he might not give her the Christmas presents because he might get muddled.'

'I don't think he will,' said Jack. 'But I have an idea. Why don't we go and tell Jennifer to put her birthday presents downstairs, then when he comes to her bedroom he can't get muddled?'

Stan said, 'I was just going to say that. I'll tell Jennifer about my idea.'

Jack smiled at Stan and said, 'Fine.'

The two boys started walking to Jennifer's house, a few streets away. It was late afternoon with freezing snow on the ground and getting dark. Suddenly, the boys saw flashing lights and heard a siren shrieking. As the ambulance raced past, they wondered what was wrong. 'Hey,' said Jack, 'it's going towards Jennifer's house. Let's run.'

 They hurried along as quickly as they could. Stan slipped twice but Jack just caught him before he fell. Stan pushed his arms away. 'You don't need to keep grabbing me,' he said huffily. 'I can walk just as fast as you.'

'Okay,' said Jack. 'Oh, look.' Along Jennifer's street they could see six reindeer, an overturned sledge, bags of Christmas presents on the ground, and Father Christmas lying on his back. The ambulance men were kneeling over him.

The boys rushed to him and heard the chief ambulance man say: 'Sorry, Father Christmas, you hurt your legs badly when the sledge skidded on the snow and you will have to rest.'

Poor Father Christmas. He looked so upset. Then Jennifer and her mum rushed out of their house and her mum said, 'Let's carry him into our house and we will look after him.'

But Father Christmas shook his head. 'What about my presents? I've nearly finished but I must deliver these tonight or some children will be very disappointed.'

The chief ambulance man replied, 'I'm sorry, Father Christmas, but you can't go on the sledge in this slippery snow with those sore legs. You really will have to rest.'

Jack said, 'That's all right. We can give the presents out because there aren't many left.'

'We can't do that,' said Stan in a loud whisper. 'We'll miss Jennifer's party – and the sandwiches and cakes and biscuits and sausages and chocolates.'

Jack frowned at him and said, 'Shh.' But Jennifer's mum had heard them. She said, 'It would be splendid if the boys delivered the rest of these presents. Jennifer and I will go and get them some sandwiches, cakes, sausages, biscuits and chocolates and they can have those on the way.'

Stan rubbed his hands. 'That's a good idea,' he said, as if he had never thought of them. 'I'll hold them while Jack drives the sledge.'

'No,' said Jack. 'You drive the sledge, Stan, and I will take the presents into the houses.'

'But I've never driven even one reindeer before,' moaned Stan, 'and I can't drive six.'

''Course you can,' said Jack. 'Just shake the reins like you used to do with your hobby horse.'

Stan looked cross. He usually did what Jack wanted, but he didn't often do it properly.

He got hold of the reins, turned to look at the presents which had now been placed on the sledge and at Jack holding the first ones to be delivered. Then he reached over for a sausage from Jennifer's mum, took three, one sandwich, two biscuits, a cake and two chocolates. He put one sausage in his mouth, mumbled 'Bye, bye' to Father Christmas, who was now sitting up, took the reins in his little fingers and was about to start.

He hadn't seen naughty Cuthbert creeping up. Cuthbert always caused trouble, but mostly because he thought it was fun. Suddenly, the ambulance siren started screaming and its lights flashed. Cuthbert had slipped into the ambulance and pressed the button.

Everyone started shouting, although the siren drowned their voices, and people ran out of their houses. But worst of all, the reindeer took fright and galloped away.

Stan couldn't hold the reins because his hands were full and, as they were going so fast, Jack dropped the presents he was holding.

The ambulance men jumped into the ambulance and chased after the reindeer to help. But they were so used to driving with the siren and flashing lights that they forgot to turn them off. So the faster they drove, the faster the reindeer ran.

They went on and on, round and round, with Stan and Jack holding on to the sledge tightly. Stan's eyes were closed and he shouted to Jack, 'I'm getting dizzy.' But when Jack looked at him he was holding the sledge with one hand and feeling for another sausage – which he found and popped into his mouth.

'Never mind the sausages,' shouted Jack. 'Get hold of the reins.' But this time Stan didn't do what Jack wanted. He finished the sausage and started feeling around with his spare hand for a chocolate.

The reindeer still raced round and round but gradually they became exhausted. Fortunately, the ambulance men remembered to switch off the siren and flashing lights, and, as they followed quietly, the reindeer eventually came to a stop.

'That was terrible,' said Jack.

'Yes, it was terrible,' mumbled Stan. He was now eating a biscuit and said, 'That was awful because I dropped my cake and things.'

Jack chuckled, 'You had lots and lots of things. You shouldn't be so greedy.'

'You see,' said Stan, 'it's a good job I'm helping with this because Jennifer won't get muddled now because of my idea.'

Jack said, 'There's one thing you are muddled about, Stan.'

'What's that?' asked Stan suspiciously.

'Well,' said Jack, 'you are in the wrong room now. Downstairs in the next room are Jennifer and her mum, and Father Christmas, and lots and lots of sandwiches, cakes, sausages, biscuits and chocolates.'

So both boys rushed in to enjoy the end of Jennifer's strange birthday party and the beginning of a really lovely Christmas.

Nanette Newman

ACTRESS

CHRISTMAS IS UPON US

Oh! Christmas is upon us
  It can't be – but it is.
The time's gone by so quickly
  and now I'm in a tizz.
The shops are over-crowded,
  The people snarl and grump,
The cards I've sent have rhymes unmeant
  (I've really got the hump!)
The food list seems quite endless,
  I'll be cooking all the day.
The turkey's just a nightmare
  and – my Aunt Meg comes to stay!

Last year – Jack was – well! – quite sleazy,
  Kept on singing really flat.
He brought his beastly snappy dog
  Who sicked up on the mat.
The children were all tearful,
  They'd been up since five o'clock,
And Ben kept telling dirty jokes
  In order just to shock.

My Mother was all mournful
  Saying things were not the same
That 'Christmas had no meaning'.
  Oh! I thought I'd go *insane*.

Then – Jane tried to flirt with Martin.
   Well! I had to look away.
The Brussels sprouts were soggy
   and it seemed an endless day.

The tree – for some strange reason –
   Simply fell on top of Kate.
Feeling jolly in this season?
   Just the thought makes me feel faint.

My present didn't fit me,
   It was really much too small.
And Grandad tripped on Jessie's skates
   and had a nasty fall.

So,

I won't believe it's Christmas
   Even though I know it's true.
I don't want to have another –
   (Well! Not for a year or two).
I need time to recover
   from the nightmare of last year.
So forgive if – if I'm not *too* glad
   that Christmas time is here.

P.S.
   But – Well –
   It does have its nice moments
   When the children are in bed
   and we've laughed at dear old Johnny,
   Played charades until we're dead,
   and the dieting is promised
   after just one more mince pie,
   and I've crossed-my-heart
   I'll never buy poor Peter another tie,
   and we're sitting all together,
   friends and family about,
   and someone brings up memories
   Yes – that's what it's all about.

Remember that cold Christmas
When Phil was only three
and he wouldn't – simply *wouldn't*
sit on Santa Claus's knee
And when Clare longed for a hamster,
and we said the answer's 'No',
Then on Christmas morning – Oh! her face,
when she saw it wasn't so.
That Christmas when – and
So it goes – 'Another glass of wine?'
Perhaps – they're really not *that* bad
These Christmases of mine.

Dame Barbara Cartland DBE DStJ

NOVELIST

I think every child's first memory of Christmas, if she is lucky and has a happy home, is of presents.

The first present I ever remember was when I was two years old, and received a present of a doll's house from my grandmother, who was a direct descendant of King Robert the Bruce of Scotland.

I can still remember going into her bedroom because she was ill, and there was the doll's house at the bottom of the bed. It seemed to me to be enormous.

It opened and of course it was two storeys with kitchens, drawing rooms, bedrooms, and contained tiny dolls. I think that, at the age of two, made me love big houses for the rest of my life.

I also remember the stocking I used to find at the end of my bed when I woke up on Christmas morning.

My father and mother had crept in very quietly and had filled one of my father's shooting stockings, which were, of course, large and long.

The difficulty for every child is not to wake up too early and enjoy the presents in the dark. But one goes to bed thinking that Father Christmas will really come.

Another vivid memory of Christmas is of walking through the snow when it was still dark to attend Holy Communion at our village church, which at that time was the famous Tewkesbury Abbey.

I shall never forget the feeling of sanctuary as one entered the huge building to find the aisle with its great round Norman pillars in darkness and the light concentrated on the altar at the east end.

It was then, I think, that I felt an awakening to the spiritual reality of Christmas which has been unforgettable.

I remember particularly that at Christmas my mother read me the story of the nativity in a child's book with lovely pictures, so that it remained for ever in my mind, mixed up with the fairies that I read about at other times.

I think every child likes to think that he or she has a special angel in heaven looking after him or her, and I was very conscious that I had my guardian angel, and I talked to him when I was unhappy, worried or anticipating something exciting.

Another most important thing at Christmas is the Christmas tree. We always had a natural green one and I still prefer that to any artificial one. They first came to England at the suggestion of Queen Adelaide, wife of William IV.

She was young when she married an old man but she brought him great happiness. While she had no children of her own, Queen Adelaide became very fond of the ten children King William had fathered by the actress Mrs Jordan, whom he could not marry because she was not of royal blood.

Queen Adelaide has, ever since her reign, enlivened all our Christmases with the tree that is a delight to every child.

Most family trees have special decorations which are handed down year after year. On top of the tree in my house is the fairy which I had on my first Christmas tree in 1901.

My mother had packed it away carefully all through the years and it glitters and smiles at us still every Christmas. When I die it will doubtless go on bringing good luck and happiness to my grandchildren and great-grandchildren.

The carol singers used to come round the day before Christmas and it is the child's job to take round the sweets or the mince pies which are made for each singer, a job which I did when they came.

Every year we had our presents arranged in our drawing room on different chairs.

We always had our own chairs and of course it was very exciting the night before when they were laid out, to see who had the most gifts and we were always reminded that the best presents came in small parcels!

It is a tradition that is still carried on by me today, although the number of chairs has grown as my family has grown.

After we had all been to church to the family service at which we would all have been very disappointed if we did not sing 'Hark! The Herald Angels Sing!' and 'The First Noël' we would hurry home to start opening our presents, some of which had been collected during the year.

Apart from the presents one receives, every child should have an idea of what presents she must give, because this teaches her how much other people must be thanked for what they have done.

Of course, Nanny used to have one of the best presents, as did Mummy and Daddy for whom, if one is well brought up, one makes something special.

I not only made special things for my mother and father, which I was taught to do by my governesses, but I also drew and painted them a special Christmas card all on my own, which was not very artistic, but it meant a lot to me and to my parents.

I think the idea of giving at Christmas is very important for children. If they have any friends they should try to think of special presents for them. It is not a question of money, but what you could paint and make yourself.

I know as a child I drew little pictures and I also, when I was allowed to, painted stones, shells and other things and gave them as presents too.

One of the things I did was to write my first book at the age of five, as a present for my mother at Christmas; it was called 'The Little Slide-Maker'. I also illustrated it, and I still have it. It has been on show on various occasions. It is not a very great artistic effort, but my mother loved it.

As I said, Christmas must be a time for children to give as well as receive and of course to be exceedingly grateful for what they receive. I remember being made to write 'Thank You' letters immediately I received a gift, something I still do today.

At Christmas we had the traditional luncheon of turkey with all its accessories, plum pudding and mince pies.

The most important person not to forget is the person who has made the Christmas cake and the Christmas pudding, and I was always sent into the kitchen to thank the cook.

I did the same with my children, as they grew up, and now my grandchildren go to thank whoever has made the special meals for them and the special Christmas dishes.

I remember we used to have a little ceremony in the evening which, to us, was the climax of a very lovely Christmas. After dinner we sat round the fireside and started by singing songs which my mother loved as a girl and which were part of her history.

'Goodbye Dolly, I must leave you' was the popular tune when she was young and all her young men went off to fight in the Boer War. 'You Are My Honey-Honeysuckle, I Am The Bee' was popular at the time she fell in love with my father and they got married. It is, perhaps, the reason why I am so keen on honey!

Many other beautiful old melodies brought back to her times which were happy or sad but are now nostalgic and very precious memories.

We sang our own songs right up to the 'pop' music of the day and after that we read our poems.

These were very special private poems written only for the family with family jokes and family teasing which everyone enjoyed! Then it was 'Auld Lang Syne' and off to bed.

My grandchildren's first effort when they were old enough was to sing a carol for me which they rehearsed themselves and they did it as a duet. That I thought was a very good effort on the part of young children.

I know my mother would then say a prayer, not only in gratitude for the past year but for the coming one, that her family would not only keep the unity and love which had been theirs at Christmas but also that they would, all of them, have happiness and good health.

Jilly Goolden

DREAM DONKEY

For some peculiar reason, Jez always felt he was the odd one out in his family. He just didn't seem to belong. His older sister, Natasha, was all right. She belonged like mad. She was Miss Perfect, Miss Perfect in Every Way. And she kept her room neat and tidy and their mother liked things tidy as could be.

George, the baby, wasn't very tidy. He was always being sick everywhere and losing his socks. But somehow that didn't seem to matter with Mum. 'Give him a chance, he's only a baby,' she would say. 'He's only just arrived.'

He'd actually arrived a few months ago now; it was just at the end of the holidays. Jez remembered how annoyed he'd been, having to come back in a hurry from the beach. He'd built a great castle that day and the sea was just about to flood the moat. 'Can't we wait for just one more wave?' he'd pleaded. But no, Mum said they had to go this minute – she'd nearly exploded when she said, 'This minute' – 'This minute because the baby's on the way.'

It was more or less then that Jez (his real name was Jeremy, but Jeremy didn't sound so cool) decided that perhaps he didn't really belong any more. That and the fact his mother was always nagging about the state of his room and his father about his work at school. He was kind of on his own in the world, now, he felt (or might as well have been), squished between Miss Perfect and Boy George. And that's how Dream Donkey came into his life.

There was a donkey living in a field near Jez's house. It wasn't a very co-operative donkey, even though Jez tried very hard to be friends.

When he went out to see it one day after school to discuss the difficulty he'd had with his tables, it just turned its back on him and stomped off in a huff. Rotten, useless donkey, he thought. Just when I hoped you'd always be my friend. As he turned for home, kicking the shrivelling autumn leaves by the path quite hard with his wellington boots, he felt extremely cross and annoyed.

Natasha and George didn't have donkey friends of their own – and now it seemed neither did Jez. He wanted so badly to have a real-life living animal friend, but the black donkey in the field next door didn't seem to feel the same way. He looked in at the kitchen window when he got back to the house and saw Natasha sitting at the table finishing the painting she had started before he left. His mother was waving a rattle at George, who was grinning as always, wobbling up and down in his bouncy chair. He'd told them before he went out about his amazing new friend, the donkey, but luckily it didn't look as though they'd seen that it was actually rather less amazing than he'd hoped. 'How was the donkey, Jez?' asked his mother. 'Brill,' he fibbed. 'He follows me everywhere. He's a real friend.'

Up in his room, littered with bits of train track, cars (some with their wheels missing) and torn magazines, he swished everything off the table with his sleeve and settled down with a piece of paper and a pencil to draw. Normally he wasn't a great one for drawing and quiet things like that. But he wanted to picture the donkey as it had been in his dream last night: soft and woolly and snuggly and standing stock still – almost welcoming – as he stretched out his arms to give it a hug. It wasn't a bad picture as it turned out and he decided to keep it secretly tucked away under his pyjamas in his top drawer.

Every day he went off to visit the grumpy old donkey in the field when he got back from school, but very rarely did it allow him to get anywhere near. When he got back home, though, he'd take out the drawing from the drawer and talk to it as if it were real. It was getting very dark in the evenings now and so his field visits had to be quick. But up in the warmth of his room he spent hours with his imaginary friend, Dream Donkey, as he had named him, the donkey of his dreams.

A few days before Christmas, when Jez's mother and older sister were getting the Christmas decorations out of the big brown box where they were locked away for an infuriatingly large stretch of the year, Jez asked if this time he could be the one to put out the crib. He'd always loved the crib. He possibly loved it even more than the brilliant gold and glitter angel with moving, whispering wings, that went on top of the Christmas tree.

As cribs go, it wasn't that special really, just scuffed plaster of Paris figures very roughly painted and some a little bit chipped. There were three standing shepherds, one carrying a small lamb under his arm, two kings (the third, the one carrying Frankinstinct, or whatever it was called, had been broken when he was dropped), a bearded Joseph, a pretty crouching Mary, a manger, an oddly humpbacked cow, two tatty sheep and the sweetest little donkey in the world, black with a roughly painted blue blanket on its back and an extraordinary beaming smile.

In the box, though, it didn't look much, even Jez had to admit. But when you arranged them properly on a table on the bit of red velvet Mum kept specially for the crib, then you were talking real magic. In many ways, putting it up was the best part of Christmas, really. And this year Jez had decided that, more than anything in the world, he wanted to be the one to put it up. Natasha, of course, wasn't too pleased when Mum surprisingly said yes. Why should Jez do the crib on his own? Why couldn't they share? But no, Mum said this year Jez could do the crib all by himself while Natasha supervised the decorating of the tree.

Beside the donkey's field there was a bank, carpeted in moss. The moss was the brightest fairy green and as soft as a velvet pincushion Jez had found in his grandmother's house. The next day when Jez went out to see the donkey, he took with him, in secret, a slim letter-opening knife. All the time he pretended he was talking to the donkey, he dug away under the moss until he'd cut out a piece of green carpet in a luxuriant square.

He carried it carefully under his jacket back to the house and laid it out, like an expert carpet fitter, wall to wall in a box turned over on its side. The inside walls and roof he painted in midnight blue and he cut stars out of sticky white paper and stuck them on the paint. Once the crib figures were set in, comfortably settled on the moss, he cut a tiny hole in the top of the box with the point of the scissors so the table light above would shine through in a beam on to the manger.

He couldn't believe that he, Jez, had created such a glorious sight. Before he called the others to come and see, he picked up the smiling donkey and moved him next to the manger so that he, too, picked up a ray of the light. When his father came home, everyone agreed that Jez had done a truly brilliant job.

On Christmas Eve, before going up to bed for the very last time, Jez said a final goodnight to the plaster of Paris donkey in the box. It seemed to smile as usual, lit up warmly in the beam of light shining in from the top of the box. He said a last goodnight, too, to Dream Donkey at the bottom of his underclothes drawer.

Snuggled under the bedclothes, trying to get to sleep on this, the biggest night of the year, his head was full not of Father Christmas like most other children in the world, but of soft cuddly donkeys instead.

Natasha was the first one up on Christmas morning and dashed into Jez's bedroom to see if his stocking was bulging full as well. They sat on the bed together, opening their presents quietly, while George and their parents slept. Jez tried to keep the biggest present to last, but somehow his fingers started ripping at the paper before he entirely meant them to. Out from the wrapping poked a bit of black fur, and then a piece of gold-threaded cloth. One last rip and it was out, the most beautiful black donkey you ever saw, its back neatly covered with a piece of rich and splendid cloth.

Not minding a bit now if Natasha discovered the existence of Dream Donkey in his secret hiding place tucked away under his pyjamas and pants, he rushed to the drawer to find the picture of his dreams. Tossing socks and his school tie untidily on to the floor, he grabbed the piece of paper he knew so well. But to his utter surprise he hardly recognized the picture he had drawn. On its skimpy black back there now was stuck the most beautiful piece of blue embroidered cloth.

This was magic, Christmas magic, and he flew downstairs, to Natasha's utter amazement, to look at the crib. He'd guessed right, because there was the smiling donkey just where he'd left him the night before, but now wearing not just his old chipped blue paint, but also a piece of the same glorious gold-threaded blue cloth. Very reverently, he took the smiling donkey with him back upstairs and, with all three blue-blanketed donkeys very carefully balanced in his arms, went in to wish the happiest Christmas ever to his parents in their bed.

'We love you very much, you know,' his mother said, and as he turned his head away so she wouldn't see the tears starting to well up in his eyes, he caught a glimpse of something sparkling and blue behind the trees in the field.

David Shilling

MILLINER

ONCE UPON A TIME THERE WAS A MAN WHO THOUGHT THAT EACH AND EVERY DAY SHOULD BE LIKE CHRISTMAS

Each and every day should be a little like Christmas; if you can't give gifts to everyone, how about trying an extra thank-you here and there or a smile? Let's face it, for some people it's very hard to be really happy on 25 December itself. I don't mean because of that disappointment when you don't like the colour of the scarf, and you didn't want a scarf in the first place, or the frustration you feel because you got diamonds, when you've got enough of those already and what you really needed was sapphires. Sometimes it's really hard to celebrate 'to order', and somehow knowing that you ought to because everyone else is makes it that bit harder still. For instance, I still recall the Christmas when my grandmother had just died. That was a really hard one. Even if all yours have been happy ones, you must know someone, even some child, whose Christmases have not been. Of course most of mine have been great except that the worst for me was the time when I was involved in an armed robbery at my home early on the morning of Christmas Eve. To try to calm me the policeman later kept repeating how lucky I was to be alive, which unfortunately had exactly the opposite effect, and I spent the whole holiday in tears. What the policeman meant to say was, 'It could have been much worse.' And of course it could have been, and I got over it. Compared with what some other people's problems are, it wasn't that bad. One of my closest friends was a war refugee at seven years old; hearing gunfire instead of carols is all wrong. But being that close to death did bring a gift with it for me – it put into clearer perspective the real value of material possessions. Even so, that is not the real moral of this story. The thing we should all remember is that even if we could convince robbers to go on strike on Christmas Eve, we can't stop horrid things happening sometimes in the run-up to the holiday season, so instead let's all determine to make this a happier place each and every day (and the nights too!) and be a bit more generous, caring and thoughtful all year round.

And right now that thought is really the only gift I can give to you, not just for Christmas but for every day. But I don't expect you to be good all of the time, so if you want to paint your face, put your clothes on back to front and run round the neighbourhood playing a guitar with a tree on your head, or whatever – just this once you can! After all – if anyone complains, just tell them it's Christmas – and I said so!

Sally Gunnell

ATHLETE

I met my husband Jon when we were both nineteen. He was the middle of three brothers: Chris was three years older and studying at Brighton Art College; Matt was four years younger and attending the local high school. Gradually, throughout the summer I got to know the Bigg family very well, spending time in Brighton. We all got on very well and had lots of laughs: we appeared to have the same sense of humour. As Christmas approached there was talk as to how we would spend it. Christmas Day in Brighton was decided by us youngsters and then there was the suggestion of fancy dress.

Well, I just knew straight away what I would dress as . . . My dad is a farmer in Essex and each year he breeds turkeys for the Christmas market. So when the day came for the turkeys to be plucked, I was to be found in the shed selecting only the finest feathers! I then spent several days sewing them on to a long-sleeved leotard, using the long tail-feathers along the arms to form wings. I planned to wear cream-coloured tights, a white swim cap and a cardboard beak. My outfit was complete – a Christmas turkey!

I managed to keep this a big secret from the Bigg boys. Whenever we met, there were big wind-ups as to what each was going to wear. Christmas Day dawned and I arrived in Brighton with my fancy dress hidden in a bag (a large bag). After Christmas dinner it was decided to hold the fancy dress parade with Jon's mum and dad as judges. So upstairs I went to change. It took quite a time to struggle into my feathered leotard – they are difficult enough at the best of times!

Tights on, swim hat on and finally the beak – off I went down the stairs, frightening Jon's cat in the process!

I burst into the living room only to find Jon and his brothers still in their ordinary clothes completely collapsed with laughter. They had had no intention whatsoever of dressing up, and had utterly taken me in all along! And there I was completely encased in turkey feathers!

You can imagine the laugh we had. It still amazes me that I stayed with Jon and even married him!

Still, I must say that I have got even with each one of those Bigg boys one by one. How? Well now, that's another story.

Wendy Cope

AT CHRISTMAS

(sung to a calypso beat)

At Christmas, at Christmas,
All over the world at Christmas,
People tell the story
Of a star that shone out bright.
And as we think of it,
Once again there's light.
And as we think of it,
Once again there's light.

At Christmas, at Christmas,
All over the world at Christmas,
People tell the story
Of Mary's baby boy.
And as we think of him,
Once again there's joy,
And as we think of him,
Once again there's joy.

At Christmas, at Christmas,
All over the world at Christmas,
People tell the story
Of our Saviour in the hay.
And as we think of him,
Love is born today.
And as we think of him,
Love is born today.

Henry Cooper OBE KSG

BOXER AND ENTERTAINER

During the war years, when food and everything was short and in great demand, our mum always made sure that my brothers and I did not go without and ensured that we had a marvellous Christmas. I remember one year in particular when Mum managed to get some pressed dates and we all tucked into them until we were sick! Despite all that was happening around us, Mum made sure that Christmas was always a memorable occasion for us all.

David Bellamy

BROADCASTER AND BOTANIST

Christmas will always be a time to be with the family, of going to church, believing in Father Christmas and listening to the Queen's speech and dreaming of snow. The strangest I ever spent was as leader of a Royal Society Expedition to Aldabra in the Indian Ocean: hot sun, coral sands and the companionship of giant tortoises, flightless rails, my fellow divers and the local fishing community from the Seychelles, Archange Michael, Georges, Harry and their wives and children. Lee Kenyon decorated the palm-leaf church with life-size cardboard figures of the nativity, their faces those of our little community. Santa came bearing gifts made from cast-off shells and bird rings and coconuts. The coconut palm has many uses – most of them make you a little more than merry. The highlight of the proceedings came when a number of the shell presents got up and walked away, each having been annexed as a new home for a land hermit crab. The day was rounded off with a dive in Grand Channel, complete with turtles, sharks, manta rays and the host of fish and corals that make such pristine places heaven here on earth.

Bill Beaumont

SPORTSMAN AND BROADCASTER

I can always remember a Christmas Day when my parents and grandparents booked a table at a local restaurant for Christmas lunch. We arrived at the restaurant at approximately 1 p.m. as we were the second sitting.

Obviously people dining at the first sitting were not in a rush to leave the table, which resulted in our family waiting until 3 p.m. By this time we decided it wasn't worth waiting and the family went home to have our Christmas lunch, which was a tin of pea and ham soup!

Rolf Harris

ENTERTAINER AND ARTIST

In Perth, where I was born and brought up, we used to get temperatures like 104°F on Christmas Day. When Mum had finished cooking the traditional turkey and all the trimmings, you could hardly exist in the house it was so hot, so we used to have our Christmas dinner down in the garden in the shade of the trees and it always used to strike me as very strange that the radio would be playing songs about jingle bells and snow and ice whilst perspiration was dripping off the end of your nose into the mashed potatoes!

I can remember Mum always used to say, 'Now, don't go into the river for about two hours after you have finished the meal.' We would say, 'Yes, Mum', and rush straight down for a swim.

In later years, this slightly bemused feeling about Christmas songs and the temperature in Australia during Christmas led me to write an Australian Christmas song with an American friend. The song was called 'Six White Boomers'. A 'boomer' is slang for a big male kangaroo, presumably because of the noise they make as they go crashing through the bush when they hop away quickly. The song, as I always tell people at my concerts, is an Australian Christmas song that a friend of mine and I wrote in 1960, based on an old Australian Christmas legend, which we had written only the previous week.

Raymond Blanc

TARTE TATIN, FAÇON CECILE
UPSIDE-DOWN CARAMELIZED APPLE TART

This dessert was part of a most memorable autumn meal put together by a dear friend, who kindly gave me her recipe. It is sumptuous, decadent and so good ... and I hope that Cecile will forgive me for having slightly changed the recipe.

The tart can be made half a day in advance and kept at room temperature. It can be reheated for 15 minutes in an oven preheated to 180°C/350°F/Gas 4.

It is important to use Granny Smith apples as they are very firm, have a high degree of acidity and a delicious taste; they will hold together beautifully.

SERVES 8
150 g (5 oz) best quality puff pastry
300 ml (10 fl oz) double cream
or lots of clotted cream (optional), to serve

FOR THE FILLING
1.8 kg (4 lb) Granny Smith apples (approx. 12 apples)
60 g (2¼ oz) unsalted butter, diced
2 pinches of powdered cinnamon
135 g (4¼ oz) caster sugar

FOR THE CARAMEL
75 g (3 oz) caster sugar
30 g (1¼ oz) unsalted butter

1. Roll the puff pastry out on a lightly floured surface to about 2–3 mm (up to ⅛ in) in thickness. Place on a tray lightly dusted with flour and refrigerate for 30 minutes.

Cut out a circle 26 cm (10½ in) in diameter (slightly larger than the dish) and refrigerate until required.

Preheat the oven to 190°C/375°F/Gas 5.

2. Peel all the apples. Cut eight of them in half vertically, and scoop out the cores. Cut the remaining four apples into quarters and remove the cores. Reserve, covered.

3. Put the caster sugar in a *tarte tatin* mould or a round cake tin, 24 cm (9½ in) in diameter and 5 cm (2 in) deep, and place over a medium heat until the sugar turns a dark caramel colour. Turn off the heat and stir in the butter. Cool down for a few minutes.

4. Place the 16 halves of apple upright around the mould, rounded side to scooped-out side, and arrange the quarters in the middle. Press the apple halves tightly together so that there are no gaps. (The apple halves will rise above the rim of the mould, by approximately 3 cm/1¼ in.)

Dot the apples with the diced butter. Mix the cinnamon with the caster sugar and sprinkle over the apples.

5. Bake the tart in the preheated oven for 25 minutes.

Remove it from the oven and place the puff pastry circle on top of the apples, tucking the edge of the pastry inside the mould. Cook for a further 30 minutes.

Remove the tart from the oven and allow to cool down for 30 minutes.

6. Turn the tart out on to a flat serving dish, pastry side down, and serve it with lots of fresh double cream or, even better, clotted cream – blissfully delicious!

When building the tart, the apples have to be packed tightly together so that there are no gaps; this ensures that the tart will hold together well.

The round of pastry must be placed *loosely* over the apples; do not try to stick the pastry to the mould. The steam produced by the apples, and not allowed to escape, would give a soggy texture to the pastry.

Simon Williams

ACTOR AND WRITER

I'LL BE THERE

Jack knew that Santa's Grotto was a treat, something that his mother wanted him to enjoy, something that called for washed hands and the putting on of a clean T-shirt, but, standing in the queue, all he could think of was the disappointment of not seeing his dad. Saturday morning was their time together when they would either play football or make up stories. His father was always pleased to see him, always jolly, with something interesting in his pocket. Dad never seemed to worry about dirt or eating greens, and when he said, 'I'll always be there, I'm your dad', Jack trusted him. However cross Mum got during the week, there was always the thought of Saturday morning with Dad. He'd rather have his usual hamburger with Dad than spend all this time waiting to see Father Christmas. (Jonty had told him that it wasn't real anyway: 'It's all pretend, Dumbo, like the tooth-fairy.') It never worried him that Dad was not allowed into the house any more and when Mum said rude things about him it never bothered him.

As he traipsed towards the stupid grotto Jack wondered what his father could be up to. What could be more important than their Saturday together? Always his dad would greet him with a great bear hug, always he smelt of dogs and cigarettes, sort of musty but nice. Always he would look at him and say, 'Hi there, Kiddo. How's tricks?' But today, according to Mum, something had 'cropped up'. Jack had heard her grumbling to Gran on the telephone, 'Bloody actors, they're all the same: never there when you want them, always there when you don't.' Jack noticed that her neck usually went red when she talked about Dad. It was all part of this stupid divorce thing; he couldn't see why people bothered with it. 'You're next, young man,' said Santa's assistant as she took his ticket. 'Go on, don't be shy. Sit on Father Christmas's lap and tell him what you want.' For Mum's sake Jack thought he had better make a show of enjoying the 'nice treat to make up for not seeing that s-h-one-t.'

'Ho, ho ho,' said the great beaming figure as Jack approached. 'And what's your name?' Jack allowed himself to be picked up by the silly old pretend Santa Claus. 'My name is Jack Butterworth and I don't believe in you,' he said as he found himself plonked in the lap of the white-bearded old gentleman. 'Don't you indeed?' Jack looked into Santa's eyes smiling above the rosy cheeks and great white beard. 'No, you're just pretend. I want to be with my dad.' Father Christmas smiled and Jack smiled back even though his front teeth were all missing. There was a familiar smell that Jack couldn't quite place, a musty smell of dogs and cigarettes. Santa Claus held Jack firmly in his arms for a moment. All the crossness Jack felt about his dad and this 'cropped up' thing seemed to go away, and there was nothing pretend in the way Father Christmas whispered, 'Hi there, Kiddo. How's tricks?'

Thomas Cunningham

MUSICIAN

Obviously I don't remember my first couple of Christmases. You see, I was otherwise occupied trying to figure out how to walk, talk and understand the concept of life from such a low vantage point.

But by age two and a half, Christmas made perfect lucid sense. I can still visualize it now' twenty-nine years later.

There I was, wrapped up warm, snug as a bug sitting bolt upright in my own four-wheeled transport (a big Silver Cross pram), Mum (my chauffeur) pushing and guiding me through the wonderland of cold, wet streets in Glasgow's city centre.

The icy air was making my breath visible, making my face sting and my pulse race. I didn't feel the cold, of course, I was far too excited for that, my cheeks a rosy flushed red. Everything had a glow to it. A halo surrounded every street light, everything was somehow magical and alive.

My normally homely front room was now transformed into a colourful tinsel-lined Santa's Grotto.

Every main street had huge neon reindeer and Santas hanging from lamppost to lamppost. Even the Woolworths shop that had always been full of big-people stuff like bulbs, socks, scarfs, hats, screwdrivers, records, nylons, plates, cups and lots more useless stuff was now full of nothing but toys, toys, toys – millions of them, as far as my tiny eyes could see – toys, toys, toys, and *I wanted them all*.

Even at that tender age I knew the importance of having an Action Man or a Hornby train set or

a three-wheeler bike. Your social standing could be greatly enhanced in my street by ownership of such an item.

Shop windows were ablaze with tinsel, trees and fairy lights, fake snow and dummies dressed as Santa. Every house had a tree at the window inviting your imagination to wonder what toys lay inside.

All the people on the bus or on the streets had a glint in their eye and everything felt so good and I was *happy*.

The world was a wonderful place. Why couldn't every day be Christmas?

It wasn't until my thirteenth or fourteenth birthday that my philosophy changed, the main reason being that I was then expected to save up pocket money and buy presents for everyone else.

When you have got to save for months and months and then wait for a late bus in the freezing Scottish winter, just to go to town to spend your own hard-saved money on your sisters and wait even longer for a bus to take you home in that bone-grinding cold, and then do the same again day after day until you have bought something for everyone, and then spend hour after hour wrapping it up, tagging it all to put under the tree ready for Christmas morning and, come Christmas morning, what do you get? You get socks, jumpers, underwear and a premature bottle of Old Spice. After all of this effort and discomfort, Christmas loses some of its appeal.

Between the ages of thirteen and nineteen it gradually goes from bad to worse: the older you get, the less you get, the more you spend the harder … it becomes a never-ending cycle, freezing half to death for other people to enjoy your hard-earned money.

The world was a horrible place. I wish it was never Christmas.

And now! Well, now I'm a thirty-two-year-old married man, older and much wiser.

My front room is like Santa's Grotto again. Everything has that special sparkle again. I don't seem to feel the cold so badly any more and every shop I go into has nothing but toys, toys, toys – millions of them – and *I want them all*.

Not for me, you understand, but for my two young children! One is aged three and the other is aged eight months.

Now I'm the chauffeur and I'm the Santa and all my feelings of excitement and wonder have returned once more.

I love it all, every last moment of this very wonderful time of year, from the church service with little baby Jesus in his crib, the presents under my tree, the tinsel, fairy lights and fake snow to the shopping in the freezing cold of winter.

But most of all I love to see my children's faces on Christmas morning as they open their presents, wide-eyed, wide-mouthed and speechless.

The world is a wonderful place. Why can't every day be Christmas?

Mr Blobby

PERSONALITY

CHRISTMAS IN CRINKLEY BOTTOM

People always ask me, 'If you're a Blob, how do you spend Christmas?' Well, being seven foot tall, luminous pink with yellow spots, having no hair and wobbly green eyes does not mean I don't celebrate Christmas. I do. I've got a big heart – no brain, but a big heart – and I love presents, Christmas and Noel Edmonds like everyone else. The only difference is I don't celebrate it in the same way. I celebrate Christmas in Crinkley Bottom.

Before I met Noel, I thought Christmas was the same throughout the country. You know: tinsel, mince pies, presents, walks in the cold, the Queen's speech, James Bond, Christmas dinner as the only meal of the year when you willingly eat Brussels sprouts, the repeat of the Queen's speech and a long, slow descent into the back of the sofa for the evening's television. Well, I was wrong. That's not Christmas in Crinkley Bottom.

Crinkley Bottom is a funny old place to be anyway. It's a sleepy, some would say unconscious, two-tractor village somewhere between Basingstoke and the Bronze Age. There's hardly anything to do there. In fact, there's so little to see, it tends to attract sightseers with only one eye.

The sign at the start of the High Street reads: 'Welcome to Crinkley Bottom. Your biggest day out ever. We have everything here. Sheep, hills, puddles, pot-holes, sheep, trees, sheep, hedgehogs, wellingtons, hedgehogs stuck to wellingtons, sheep, grass and little miniature tombstones which mark the holes on the crazy golf course'.

Crime's a big problem as well. Especially burglary. In fact, Crinkley

Bottom is the only place I know that, when you go to buy stockings, they ask you for your head size.

It was during a spate of burglaries by One-Foot Frank – so called because he only ever left one footprint at the scene of the crime – that I received my first ever invitation from Noel to his traditional Christmas Eve party at the Great House. Usually, every villager with any sense turns up but as there's only three villagers with any sense in Crinkley Bottom, he decided to invite all the other villagers as well. Still, I was honoured and excited to be going.

On Christmas Eve, I was having meetings at the House of Commons so I arrived in Crinkleshire rather later than expected. I pulled up outside the Great House in my pink Beetle, Blobby 1, but there were no other cars to be seen, just a row of wellingtons. Seventeen wellingtons in fact. That's eight pairs and a single green one with thermal lining. Oh heck, I thought to myself, the mayor's here.

The 'ding-dong' door bell just 'donged' when I pressed it and then all the verses to 'Silent Night' played at 600 decibels before Noel opened the door and let me in. There was a cheer from everybody as I entered and then a nice friendly groan as they realized who it was.

'You're just in time,' said Noel with his big white woolly coat on that makes him look like a cloud. 'Has that coat got a silver lining?' I asked but the joke went right over his head. 'We're off down to the High Street to watch the Christmas pantomime,' he said. So we all lined up, two by two, and walked to the local theatre – The Edmonds Memorial Hall – singing 'Supercalafragilisticexpialidocious' which, when you can only say 'Blobby, Blobby, Blobby', is a real mouthful.

The local pantomime that year – due to lack of money – was 'Puss in Bare Feet'. It was fantastic. Mrs Bulstrode played the City of London with great style. Her Trafalgar Square was magnificent. Only Tony Blackburn disappointed. His costume hadn't turned up so he played Dick Whittington with no clothes and an eye patch and though we laughed, it did detract from the plot.

Back at the house, for the first time I saw the extent of Noel's Christmas decorations. He had a thousand Christmas cards dangling on string everywhere. It was the same card photocopied a thousand times and read: 'Merry Christmas Noel. From the Noel Edmonds Fan Club'. There was also an overwhelming smell of satsumas and mixed nuts and his Christmas tree was the 400-year-old oak tree that grows through the floorboards in the living room but now was strewn with fairy lights, baubles and tinsel. Well, he never buys tinsel. He just gets Merrilegs the old butler to sneeze. I couldn't help noticing, however, that the oak did have three big presents under it, wrapped in pink paper with yellow spots. Very exciting!

'It's party time,' said Noel and then read off a list of the things we could play throughout the evening. 'Over here you can play games . . .' Well, I expected to see Scrabble or Twister but it turned out to be trampolining over an elaborate obstacle course which wouldn't have looked out of place in the Olympics. Too much for my little wobbly Blobby legs anyway.

'Over here,' he went on, 'we have Spinning the Chamberpot, Pig-Trough Surfing and Guess the Goat and the rules are . . .' Well, I sneaked off to the kitchen at this point, wondering whatever happened to those games I used to play as a baby Blob, like Blind Blob's Buff, Pin the Tail on the Mouse and that game where you race while sucking peas through a straw? I entered the kitchen to find a dozen people all sucking peas through a straw but somehow it wasn't how I remembered it.

If I was going to get into the spirit of a Crinkley Bottom Christmas, I needed a kip. Just twenty minutes' sleep to recharge my jelly and get me going again. It was half past nine at night.

At 5.30 in the morning, I was woken by Noel, standing by the bed in his Mutant Ninja Turtle pyjamas. 'Oi, Blob. I can't find my slippers.' 'Well, what do you want your slippers for?' I asked, half dazed. 'I want to go sleepwalking,' he said. Well, it's the only exercise he gets so I got up to help. I'd obviously slept through the party but I could tell by the number of peas that he'd sucked into his pyjama pocket that he'd clearly played and won that game.

'Come on, then, Noel. Let's find your slippers.' So we both crept along the hall in the dark, feeling for his Pingu slippers. Trouble was, Norman, the suit of armour, had fallen across the landing and I tripped over him and fell down the main stairs of the Great House. I stood up quickly but slipped on a broken Walnut Whip and went head first into the front door.

The door opened and as I lay on the welcome mat I'd made for Noel out of the bits left in his electric razor, I saw outside, in the snow, a man in a large red coat with a white beard and a bag over his shoulder. Noel joined me and started to rub Germolene on my sore spots but he soon stopped when I pointed to the mysterious visitor on the lawn.

Both our jaws dropped and it's fair to say we've never been able to speak properly since. We were looking at Father Christmas. There he was. In the flesh. He only had one leg but he was everything you'd expect of Santa Claus. 'Ah, isn't he sweet,' said Noel as the man ran off into the distance. 'Sweet? Yes. But where's his other leg?' I enquired in a Belgian accent. Noel looked at me. 'Well, if he's left it on the sleigh, he'll be hopping mad.'

I stood up and walked over to the oak tree. 'Noel. Where are the three Christmas presents in the pink-and-yellow-spotted paper?' We looked under the tree and then at each other. 'Santa Claus!' exclaimed Noel and ran to the door. 'That's not Santa Claus,' I said. 'My big pink cells tell me that you've been burgled . . . by the one-wellington-wearing mayor of Crinkley Bottom.' Noel gasped. 'You mean, the mayor of Crinkley Bottom is One-Foot Frank?'

Looking back, it's funny how a Walnut Whip can help solve a crime when you least expect it. The mayor went to prison. I was voted the new mayor of Crinkley Bottom and now Noel spends Christmas with his mum. She's a bouncer at the Liszt and Newt Public House.

And my three Christmas presents? We never found them but it doesn't matter. It's the thought that counts. Thanks, Noel.

Wishing you all a big wobbly Blobby Christmas from all of us at the Great House in Crinkley Bottom. And remember, a Walnut Whip is for life. Not just for Christmas.

Sheridan Morley

WRITER AND BROADCASTER

GENERATIONS OF CHRISTMAS

We are not a family who take Christmas lightly: indeed my mother has been known to call in lists of what we would each like sometime during the summer holidays on the principle that the sooner she and Harrods get through with the shopping the sooner they can start planning for Easter.

The first Christmas I can remember was about 1945: there had been some kind of a war on and people were celebrating and I was taken to a pantomime. On the way home we were walking down the Strand and a very old gentleman patted me on the head and my godfather said, 'That was George Robey', as if that explained anything.

Then there was the year of the electric trains. By this time we were in New York where Robert was doing a play and there was a firm called Lionel who made trains which, while not exactly lifesize, were about twice the dimensions of anything ever contemplated by our own Triang/Hornby lads. That particular Christmas – it must have been 1948 and there was snow in Central Park and I gave Anna Massey whooping cough (not as a present, you understand, it was just that she came to tea and I happened to have it) – was one of Robert's finest. Not a mechanical man, a failing I have alas inherited, he yet managed to rig the trains so that they ran right the way around the living room and out into the dining room and back, a distance of roughly two miles, since American living rooms tend to be large.

The sheer thrill of waiting in the living room while the train made its invisible journey around the dining room and then returned intact was quite something, eclipsing even the thrill of a huge upturned coffin thing in the corner which provided pictures and sound simultaneously at the flick of a mere seven switches.

If there is a prize for good Christmases, I reckon that 1948 gets mine; admittedly being seven helped a lot. Seven is an ideal age for Christmas: you're old enough to enjoy it but young enough not to have to do much about getting it ready or washing up afterwards. On the day itself, Robert took my mother and sister and me (my brother, ever dubious about family celebrations, had not yet been born) to Broadway to see Ray Bolger in *Where's Charley?* since it is only the English who are nutty enough to close their theatres on the one day of the year positively made for play-going. Anyway at the end of the second half Mr Bolger actually waved to me and I promised myself that I would learn to tap dance and wave to audiences, just two of the promises I have managed to overlook in the intervening half-century.

Then there was a Christmas in Australia where it was far too hot and we got sand in the mince pies and one could swim except for the munchies (or sharks as we deep-sea folk like to call them) who fancied a leg or two by way of seasonal chewing. Then we came home to Berkshire where for the last forty years we have held a series of annual celebrations planned with only slightly more care and attention than the Royal Wedding.

When my grandmother, Gladys Cooper, was alive and had a house in Henley, it was possible to progress through five totally separate households (my cousins, aunt and parents also live within ten miles of us, not intentionally, I think – it just happened like that) on a sort of gastronomic tour which could take up to five days depending on whether or not Christmas fell at a weekend. Gladys was at her best doing Christmas teas, sensational affairs since she seldom ate lunch and was therefore always ready for a good tea. At these Yuletide gatherings she would hand out the presents along with the scones and, as we grandchildren got gradually older and more tiresome to shop for, she would pass on to us a selection of her birthday presents, her birthday having fallen conveniently on 18 December (she herself had celebrated more than eighty of these anniversaries by 1970 and was finding she already had most of the things she needed). One year she passed on to me a massive log basket, having failed to notice that its original donor had filled it with all kinds of goodies like smoked salmon and Russian caviare, and for some days afterwards the family debated the ethics of whether or not the contents had technically been a present to me or an oversight on Gladys's part. I need hardly add that by the time the family upheld the latter theory I had eaten most of the salmon.

Then there was the Christmas I brought my fiancée home from America and decided to break it to my parents that they were about to lose their elder son, an event they had, I think, been keenly awaiting for some years. My mother maintains I began the conversation with, 'It's, um, about that girl upstairs . . .'

Then there was the year of my sister and the powdered glass. Told by my wife one pre-Christmas night to bring home some cranberry sauce, I drifted into a supermarket and acquired a jar marked down to half price because there was a nasty crack down one side where someone had evidently dropped it. The contents being still intact, and I being ever on the alert for a bargain especially around Christmas, I took it home and decanted it into a dish. Comes Christmas lunch, my sister was eating with us, and from her came a crunching sound not wholly consistent with cranberries; she, never one to look on the bright side, naturally assumed she was being murdered and the rest of the afternoon was spent in heated discussion of whether Agatha Christie's characters died from powdered or fractured glass. My sister has still not entirely forgiven me, but she's lucky to be alive to carry on complaining, or so I tell her.

From Robert I have inherited a deep fear of not getting enough Christmas cards, an inability to put anything together once my children have taken it to pieces, and a vague feeling that there must be an easier way of doing the whole thing if only one could find it. Still, by careful family planning it is possible to ensure that there's always one child around of mechanical device age, and once you've got him or her on your side there's no limit to the fun; my grandson has now reached the Hornby Electric age and this year will, if my credit at Harrods holds up, see some refinements to the basic track-and-one-points system that is presently gathering dust on the playroom floor.

Then there is my annual struggle with the Scorpions; this will at some future date be the subject of a five-volume Gothic novel but, for the time being, suffice it to say that one dark and stormy night twenty-five Novembers ago I acquired a set of racing cars (named Scorpions for reasons best known to Lesney Products) with a view to giving them to my son for Christmas – admittedly he was then barely three but he is a tolerant child and I thought might be prepared to indulge me. Anyway after six months' hard labour I had the track assembled in good time for the summer holidays and then tried to race the cars. They didn't. What followed was a two-year dialogue with a kindly lady at the Harrods toy department who informed me with some relief, that as Scorpions were no longer on the market there wasn't much point in my complaining about them any longer. 'I think,' she said, in one of the most memorable summaries of recent times, 'there must have been something wrong with them.'

I suppose the most peaceful Christmas I ever had was one pre-marital year when I was in Los Angeles staying with a lovely actor called Richard Haydn who always spends Christmas afternoon at the movies. That year we saw three feature films, two cartoons and a newsreel and still had time for an oven-fresh, hand-prepared, finger-licking-good dinner at a drive-in afterwards.

Things are different now of course, what with the house and the children and the cat and the goldfish (what do you give a goldfish for Christmas?) and the Christmas tree I carefully replanted last New Year's Eve and which lived all through the summer only to die a week ago, just about the time our local garden centre began selling the new ones – I think they programme them to do that. You'll have to forgive me now, I must just go and find a present for my grandson, Barnaby; do Harrods still sell Delhi Durbars, I wonder?

Martin Jarvis

ACTOR

NICKED

Many years ago, in the seventies, I met a splendid, ruddy-faced actor of uncertain years, called Nicholas. He never played big parts, he told me, but added that he liked to think his contribution to the world of make-believe was not entirely insignificant.

Indeed, in the Dickensian film we were shooting, he played a cheerful, chubby party-guest and whenever he was on the set the scene seemed almost to light up and, somehow, you couldn't take your eyes off him. Several people remarked on this fact and a fellow actor put it perfectly when he said to me: 'It's strange, old Nick doesn't have any lines and he's only in one scene, but there's something so warm and likeable about him he really makes the whole place kind of glow.'

I made a point of chatting to Nick during a break in filming and over a cup of coffee he told me, in his fruity baritone, that he'd done many things in his life. He'd been a postal worker in Australia, a chimney-sweep in Canada, and had driven various eccentric forms of transport in northern Norway. Exciting stuff and, of course, I told him something of my life in return. When I said I had two children, a house in Croydon and a Vauxhall Viva, I couldn't help thinking it sounded fairly tame in comparison. Nevertheless he was very easy to talk to and we chatted amiably on. During another wait on the set he confided to me that he was finding it increasingly difficult to keep in regular employment throughout the year and that, at Christmas time, he often had to accept an engagement at one or other of the larger London stores as 'Father Christmas'. 'Well, old son,' he twinkled, 'it's not a bad role. Splendid costume and make-up. Warm and dry. Free lunch and tea. Matinees only, ho ho! Of course, dear boy,' he lowered his voice as our director hovered near, 'I tend to keep it a secret around the studios. Not quite the thing, what? Oh no!'

At the end of that day, his last day, we wished each other luck for the future. It was November and I was soon to start a horror picture, *Taste the Blood of Dracula*. Nick had no immediate acting prospects but generously clapped me on the back and boomed, 'Good luck with the fangs, old son. And watch out for Dracula!' We shook hands and went our separate ways.

Some weeks later, as the first flurries of fine snow began to descend on London's dormitory suburbs, Toby, my five-year-old son, and I stood in front of Kennards' of Croydon. Toby's gloved hand clutched mine tightly and together we entered the orange-lit portals of Croydon's premier store. Kennards' was always exciting at Christmas: as exciting for Toby as it had been for me at the same age – and now. It had its own arcade, holly-decked and tinselled for the season. Today we walked swiftly past the weird all-year-round aquariums that contained, not fish, but penny-in-the-slot side-shows. At the drop of a pre-decimal coin, strange slow-motion dummies would act out their puppet-lives, dancing grotesquely to the sounds of an unseen hurdy-gurdy. An axe-murderer would chop up his puppet-wife in slow time, a wooden ice-skater would waltz and spin and Sweeney Todd shaved and sliced until the blood (and the money) ran out. There were real ponies that took you for a mini-ride up and down the arcade before they trotted off to their proper Christmas job – pulling Cinderella's coach in the pantomime at the Ashcroft Theatre, just up the road. And best of all (and why we were hurrying), there was Santa's Grotto. Magic! Toby and I were at one in our seasonal thoughts as we quickened our pace towards the temporary residence of this most welcome celebrity-guest. On we sped to join the fidgeting, want-to-go-to-the-loo queue of eager Santa-meeters inching nearer and nearer to that cheery chamber.

'And what's your name, little girl?' We could just hear the question from within as we stood, not yet in sight of our grotto hero.

'Melissa. And I want a Barbie doll for Christmas – with lots of outfits,' came a smug and smirking voice of tiny, pampered authority.

'Well now, Melissa,' (we strained our ears to hear), 'I'm sure I'll bring you exactly what you deserve.'

Toby and I exchanged a glance as we moved forward again to a point where we could now see Santa himself, beautifully lit, it seemed, handing over a box of dull-looking pencils to a sharp-faced six-year-old.

'Come along, young man!'

Santa held out his arms and beamed in welcome as the small boy in front of us (accompanied by his mother) marched boldly into the grotto. With Santa now fully in my sights I found myself watching him closely. And listening . . .

'What's your name, my boy?' he boomed.

'I'm Ashley,' piped this pint-sized Croydonian, who then embarked on an in-depth discussion as to how Santa managed to be in so many places at once. 'You were in Selfridges yesterday as well,' said Ashley accusingly.

'Well, my dear Ashley,' replied Santa, 'I do have a lot of back-up. Many helpers.'

Toby and I nodded at each other: of course he does, we both agreed. I looked keenly at what I could see of Santa's face and tried to imagine it without all that frosty face-fungus. I listened again to the plummy, rumbly voice. Yes . . . of course.

'Who's next? Come along.'

We made our entrance into the grotto and immediately, amazingly, Santa exclaimed, 'Hello, Toby! How are you?'

Toby grinned hugely and said he was very well, thank you. I grinned too and thought, 'Good heavens, he knew Toby's name.' But then, of course, actors have good memories and I suppose certain things stick.

'Well, well,' Santa went on. 'Young Toby Jarvis. And his dad, *Martin*!'

Toby turned and smiled at me. Brilliant. Quite brilliant, I thought. And of course Santa *would* know each child's name. And each dad, for that matter. Toby accepted the fact quite naturally and chatted away to all-knowing Santa, who indeed seemed to know a great deal about him – where he had spent his summer holidays and that he was keen on music. Wow, what a memory. Well, that filming day in November had been a long one. But how brilliant of Nick to remember.

'Happy Christmas, Toby,' said Santa, reaching into his sack, scrabbling for a moment and then drawing out a shining mouth-organ. 'I know you'll make some good tunes with this.' Toby took the glittering gift, with eyes equally bright. 'And *Martin*,' continued Santa, 'I hope Dracula is batting on nicely!'

I gasped, nodded, finally winked and said, 'Oh – yes, and thanks – very much, er – Santa.'

He winked back at me and called, 'A very Merry Christmas, old sons,' and then off we went out of that magical grotto.

'He was great, Dad, wasn't he?' said Toby, brandishing his magnificent mouth-organ as we strode down the arcade. 'He knew everything about us. Still, I s'pose that's what being Father Christmas is all about.'

'Yes,' I replied, crossing my fingers. 'I guess he just does a lot of homework.' And we made our joyful way out into the street, across the settling snow towards the car park.

A couple of months later I bumped into Nick again – in a corridor at the BBC Television Studios in Shepherd's Bush. He was dressed as a rather jolly-looking pirate and he spotted me as he hurried towards the set. 'What ho, old son,' he called, waving his cutlass. 'How are you? How's the family?'

'Oh, Nick,' I said. 'Good to see you. And, by the way, thanks for being so brilliant at Kennards', in Croydon. Toby was thrilled. It was wonderful you remembering his name and all about him, and everything.'

Nick smiled and looked at me oddly for a moment. Then he put a finger to his lips and said, 'Good-oh. Well, must go. Got to swash me buckle. Good to see you, dear boy.' He hurried to the door leading to the set, opened it, then suddenly turned and said: 'Actually, Martin, I didn't do Santa at Christmas. Not this time. Got a panto job up north. I was in Leeds all December and January. Made a break from the grotto. Ho-ho. Well, cheeri-bye.' And he was gone.

Well, I suppose, must have been, could it have been – no – the real one we saw in Croydon, after all?

Or . . .

I guess, Nick, you're a saint.

Doc Cox

BROADCASTER AND MUSICIAN

The problem with Christmas is that they have it at such an inconvenient time of year. Wouldn't it be more economical if they had it just after the January sales?

Perhaps they could shift it backwards, combining it with Guy Fawkes Night. The Christmas cards would show reindeer attempting to blow up the Houses of Parliament, and we could use the bonfire to roast the turkey, toast the pudding, and dispose of that ghastly aftershave Auntie Mavis gave us last year.

At the moment Christmas happens on the only day in the year that the tubes and buses don't run. It's darned inconvenient, but at least it's in pantomime season, I suppose.

However, looking back over a lifetime of Christmases, the ones I remember best make up this collection of magical mornings, and peppermint sheep.*

1. My dad making me a toy sweet shop. The shop was wooden but the sweets (still on coupons after the war) were real! He also gave me my first second-hand bicycle, smartened up with red paint, which unfortunately didn't dry properly until February!

2. The annual new shirt 'for best'. It scratched like an Algerian tomcat, and had a stiff collar that almost sawed your head off.

3. The Christmas when Dad made me a sledge. Grandma gave me some toy skis too. Then it didn't snow for three years!

4. The Nativity play. I was a shepherd. I remembered all my lines, but delivered them in the wrong order.

One of the Three Wise Men, wearing an exotic bedspread and a crown covered in Quality Street wrappers, announced their gifts as 'Gold, Franky Stench and Myrrh'.

A teacher friend tells me that last Christmas her Three Wise Men, all TV-generation five-year-olds, offered the Holy Infant 'Gold, Frankenstein and Blur'.

5. Mary Poppins on the telly. Featuring Dick Van Dyke as the strangely accented Cockney sweep. I was twenty-seven before I realized that he wasn't meant to be an Australian.

6. Doing a gig on Christmas Eve. We were second on the bill to an 'Italian' magician. He actually came from the incomprehensible end of Birkenhead, and had just enjoyed a glass (or fifteen) of sherry. He waved some stuffed rabbits about, and fell off the stage. Hilarious.

7. Going to Hyde Park. At 9 o'clock on Christmas morning you can watch thirty hardy souls jump into the Serpentine for their annual swim. And you thought *I* was barmy!

8. The best-ever presents. My sweetheart, Jilly, who isn't a great knitter, made me a lovely blue bobble hat. It was a bit small. In fact, it would have been tight on a tangerine.

After a year of stretching, and consultations with a family of Patagonian head-shrinkers, I finally got it to fit.

The next year she knitted a matching scarf, taking care to make it large enough. It turned out like a honeymoon-sized hammock, and grew bigger with every wash.

I believe it is now being used as a drift net by a Grimsby trawler.

9. Lord and Lady Bountiful. Our cats' Christmas stockings always seem to contain white choc-drops they won't even sniff at. The squirrels in our local park love 'em . . . so that's our Boxing Day walk taken care of!

10. Christmas Dinner. Jilly and I are vegetarian, and rather 30 disorganized cooks. For a dozen years we've attempted to get a meal on the table by lunchtime. Our closest result has been 3 p.m. (stuffed marrow and spicy parsnip surprise).

Last year, following lots of hilarity with the mulled wine, I'm afraid it was chestnut and red cabbage casserole at 7.30 p.m.

So for a Real Cool Yule, just take a selection from the list above, and mix 'em up well with lashings of Phil Spector's *Christmas Album*. (Yes, I know it was recorded thirty years ago, in Los

Angeles, in an August heatwave. But, for me, Darlene Love tearing out her tonsils on 'White Christmas' still manages to sum up the innocence and magic of this extraordinary time of year.)

With that, please let me offer my best wishes for the festive season to everyone, everywhere. (Excuse me now, I'm just off to stuff the Christmas aubergine!)

* By the way, a peppermint sheep means 'Baa! Humbug!'

Brian Conley

ENTERTAINER

Christmas was never much fun for me when I was a child. Every Christmas Eve my dad would go out into the garden, fire a shotgun in the air and then come back in and tell us Santa Claus had committed suicide. You see, we were a very poor family. We were so poor we couldn't afford central heating. At Christmas, I and my whole family would sit round a candle and if it was really cold we used to light it.

One year Mummy said to Daddy that she would like something with lots of diamonds. So Daddy bought her a pack of cards! And with money being so tight our Christmas tree was so small that Dad had to kneel down to put the star on it. I remember looking out on to the street and seeing all the children playing with their toys. A lot of the boys had bows and arrows. I was very envious, so Mummy went out and bought me a present – a T-shirt with a target on the back.

When I was a kid we never had computers; we used to make our own toys. I remember getting a piece of string, a plank of wood and four wheels from our next-door neighbours' pram and there I was as happy as Larry (it's a puppet!) in my home-made go-kart. They still make them, they're called Ladas. Or is that what you put your food in?

Anyway, the Christmas I remember most was 1969. I was eight years old and the news on that day was that the RSPCA had rescued 500 turkeys, which they were going to release as soon as they were defrosted. Which reminds me, it was that Christmas when my mother came into my room and said, 'Brian, your uncle and aunt are coming round for

Christmas dinner, and we haven't got enough food to go around. So when I ask you if you want any Christmas dinner, you say, "No thank you, Mummy." Have you got that?' With a sinking heart I replied, 'Yes Mummy.' So the time arrived, we were all sitting round the table and as rehearsed Mummy said, 'Would you like any Christmas dinner, Brian?' and I said, 'No thank you, Mummy.' But deep down I was starving. After they had all finished eating, Mum then brought out the Christmas pudding with extra-thick double cream. She said to me, 'Brian, do you want any Christmas pudding?' I looked up at her, defiantly wiping the tears from my eyes then, taking a deep breath, I shouted, 'Yes please, Mummy!' And she said, 'Well, you can't have any because you didn't eat your dinner!'

Happy days! But before I go I would like to leave you with this thought. Always remember that people in need should be given and those who don't give should be knee'd! Happy Christmas.

Toyah Willcox

BROADCASTER AND SINGER

Childhood Christmases were the most magical.

It was the appearance of the Christmas tree that cued two weeks of sheer all-encompassing joy. I'm talking about being four years old. Just able to talk but unable to comprehend the hidden meanings of the words of wisdom from the giants, the adults.

My family home, although modest, was a castle to me and everything in it was rare and precious. But the Christmas tree was proof that Nania, fairies, hobgoblins and fauns truly did exist. For the tree miraculously appeared overnight and it shed such light and a divine perfume. Being small, I could sit under it all evening with the glass baubles dancing in my face.

Christmas was a time that my brother was nice to me. Fighting was not on the agenda, only receiving.

Oh, it was perfect. I was too young to do any washing-up, too small to hoover, too innocent to be blamed when icing was picked off the uncut Christmas cake. In later years my teeth marks gave me away and punishment followed.

In retrospect my parents were miracle-workers. I totally believed in the existence of Father Christmas until an embarrassingly late age. But back then, at two in the morning, my brother would wake me to say Father Christmas had been because there were stockings on our beds, and we'd snuggle up under the blankets with torches, sworn enemies calling a truce on Christmas Day, and eat all the chocolate in our heavily laden stockings. I'd boast that I'd heard Father Christmas on the stairs and he'd pooh-pooh the very thought, being five years older than me.

In the morning Mum and Dad would play Hard to Wake Up. We'd

take them tea and biscuits in bed, made by my sister Nicola because she was eight years older and could reach the kettle. Then they'd slowly amble downstairs to the door of the lounge which had been locked by Father Christmas and wouldn't be unlocked until he knew we'd been good children. This drove me into a frenzy, because I didn't fully understand the concept of good and if this man could come all the way from Lapland and deliver our presents in one night surely he must be like God and know whether we'd been good or not. This was my first experience of guilt!

Shazam! The door would be ceremoniously opened by my father, and my brother and sister and myself would dive into what seemed a sea of treasures. My parents were unforgettably generous. There'd be a blackboard on an easel, a tricycle, *Rupert Bear* annuals, punch balls (I was determined to beat my brother in our many fracas), cowboy outfits, Etcha-Sketch, *Blue Peter* annuals – the list is endless.

Magic does exist and it's invariably performed by those people who keep their children innocent of their hard work, parents!

Christmas, to me, is a place where I wish time itself would stand still and embrace us all, for ever, in that feeling of love, security and happiness.

Julia Morley

BUSINESSWOMAN

Children in the majority of Christian countries celebrate Christmas on 25 December, the anniversary of the birth of our Lord Jesus. On that day, children receive Christmas presents, pull crackers and enjoy their turkey and Christmas pudding, or other traditional Christmas fare, such as duck or goose. Whatever the meal, to those gathered together, it is a time of happiness and rejoicing.

It is also a time to think of those less fortunate. There are children who do not get a Christmas meal. Indeed, many do not get a proper meal at any time, and in our Christmas rejoicing we should spare a thought for such children and, where possible, try to bring a little joy to those less fortunate.

Most of us have families and by tradition we all get together around our Christmas tree to open our presents and perhaps sing a carol or two. It is, therefore, rather difficult to join children elsewhere. We in the Variety Club have a Toy Fund and we distribute large numbers of toys so that thousands of disadvantaged children may have a toy for Christmas. But that is not quite the same as being with them and this was a problem which worried me years ago. How could I be with my family at Christmas and at the same time share it with some disadvantaged children?

I have been privileged to be able to visit children all over the world due to my job with the Miss World Organization. I found that children everywhere had little idea of dates or time. If you held a party in November and called it a Christmas party, children would look forward to it just as eagerly, and turkey and mince pies would taste just the same on 25 November as on 25 December. Certainly the crackers produce the same sound and the same gifts.

Each year we include a Christmas party for disadvantaged children in the country where the Miss World Pageant is staged. This year it was in South Africa. Two hundred and fifty orphaned children were invited and the contestants from eighty-five nations each hosted three children. It was tremendous fun with all the Christmas trimmings and African songs and dancing. We had a Christmas party that none of us will forget for a long time. Addresses were exchanged from all over the world so everyone could keep in touch with the children, and perhaps the most precious part to all of us was President Nelson Mandela honouring us with his presence. What a wonderful and kind man he is. He was indeed Santa to all the children and the Miss World contestants. In his inimitable fashion, President Mandela insisted on meeting and talking to everyone personally.

It was truly a world family Christmas party, proving that whoever you are and wherever you are is not important. Give an occasion a name and enter into the spirit of the occasion and it will be the real thing to those taking part.

Later in the evening, as the children went back, stacked with varying gifts, presents and mementoes of the day, the party continued on with all the eighty-five nations, mothers, fathers and fellow countrymen who joined in the second part of the world family party. Those who were able danced the typical dance of their country, such as Malaysia, Thailand and India. Others proved to be amazingly talented, with Miss Switzerland singing with a voice that one day will show her star quality. And the most remarkable thing of all was to watch the whole world applauding their efforts. With the dinner and cabaret over, the girls stayed in the party mood all through the evening and the Christmas atmosphere continued until dawn.

All this goes to show that you can enjoy Christmas even if it is not on Christmas Day. It is people who make occasions and parties. A good host or leader, good music with festive tunes and all the accessories, with balloons, hats and novelties – no matter where you are – can create the Christmas spirit.

There is, of course, another way if you cannot create a party as we did. Find out where there are children who will have no Christmas and take one or two into your home for Christmas. You will get as much joy out of it as they will.

Maggie Philbin

BROADCASTER

THE FLAT FOX

Once upon a time there was a fox. A greedy, cunning, sly old fox. A fox with a reputation for wickedness and an appetite for chickens, newborn lambs and children. No one had actually seen the fox eat children. It was generally thought that he was far, far too clever ever to be caught red-handed. But everyone knew someone, who knew someone, who'd heard from their granny, who'd never misled a soul, that this was a fox with a heart of steel, teeth like razors and a mind set on eating any child who wandered carelessly after dark in the woods at the back of the playground. Especially if they'd been told not to.

It was going to be a hard winter. The leaves on the trees were gone, the bare branches clawing in the biting wind against a sky that seemed forever grey. Three days before Christmas the snow came and the children, freed from school, heady with the excitement of presents to come, thought their happiness complete.

The fox curled up in the pale winter sunshine. Lying on the bitumen of the toolshed roof, sated with the spoils of all the dustbins in the avenue, his eyes began to close. He could hear the shouts of the children as they fought over plastic sledges, the cries as snowballs broke in their faces and the screams as wet snow was shoved down necks. Black thoughts turned in his mind. He slept and dreamt of those black possibilities.

Darkness came. Snow began to fall again, harder and faster. Protesting children were called to the warmth of kitchens and television suppers. The fox woke, disturbed by the coldness. He was stiff. He was hungry. He was tempted.

As Sally and Laura wriggled in their beds, trying to warm all the cold bits so that it was safe for their toes to explore, they talked about the fox. They talked about what they would do if they felt his hot breath on their legs, how they would hit him with the heaviest thing they could find. They talked about how they didn't really believe that a fox could eat children and how they would kill him if he tried. They had one last look out of the window. Outside in the snow, pawprints led from the toolshed, across the garden, towards the house.

'They've left the cat outside!' cried Laura. The girls ran to the back door. Pulling back the bolts, they called encouragingly to Tiger, a cat who loved the good things in life and wouldn't be impressed by a night in the snow. The door swept open and in flew a snarling mass of red fur and sharp teeth.

The fox they didn't believe in was on their doorstep, the fox who wasn't really frightening was absolutely terrifying and the fox they knew how to destroy was about to eat them. Laura remembered the plan – she reached out for the heaviest thing she could find. As the fox sank his teeth into her sister's leg she brought the metal doorstop down on him. He stopped snarling and biting and lay still. Again, she let the weight of the doorstop fall on the dull red coat. The fox was flattened. Lifeless. Together they hurled the body outside. They slammed the door. They were safe.

But outside in the snow, the fox wasn't dead. He was merely flat. And a flat fox is just as hungry, just as wicked and just as nasty as a round one.

And flat foxes aren't kept out by shut doors. They can slide underneath them. Which is just what this fox did. He slid underneath the toolshed door and bided his time.

As the lights began to go out in the houses along the street, the fox slid out of the shed, under the fence and into the garden next door. He slid up the path, under the back door, through the kitchen, along the hallway and up the stairs. He slid under the door of George Daniel David Burpett and ate him. Quickly. But when the fox came to slide out of the bedroom, he couldn't. Because, although he was flat, George Burpett wasn't. The fox would have to hide until his dinner had gone down.

Shortly after the milk bottles had rattled on the doorstep, but before the postman had crunched his way through the snow, the flat fox, flatter than ever and already feeling dangerously peckish, slid out of the house, back to the toolshed.

Nobody made snowmen that day. Children stayed inside as the legend of the fox spread from house to house, leaving a trail of fear and bewilderment in its wake.

Bedtime was tough. There were those who didn't want to turn off the lights, frightened in case the fox slid under their doors; there were those who were wildly excited, hoping to see this dark fairy-tale creature. Either way, lights didn't go out until long after the flat fox had fallen asleep, exhausted by the waiting.

It was a Christmas Eve they would always remember. Stockings were hung up. Mince pies were eaten. But children weren't asking about Father Christmas coming down the chimney, they couldn't push away the fear of the fox who might come under the door.

Hunger was gnawing at the flat fox. His eyes stared coldly, watching the house lights. As soon as they were out, he made his move. Softly he slid across the snow. Silently he slid across the doorstep where he had been so pointlessly battered by children who should know better. Up the stairs, along the landing and under the door of his sleeping tormentors.

Sally and Laura stirred, instincts sharp to the danger. When the fox leapt, hungry and powerful, they were ready for him.

'Quick, under the bed!'

Under the bed was a supply of bricks which the children hurled at the fox. Once again he was still. Seemingly lifeless and, if possible, even flatter than before.

The children carried out a plan of startling simplicity. Using the strongest glue they could find, they stuck the fox inside a book. They curled his body round on the page, so that he looked as though he were sleeping. More glue fixed his tail securely on the paper. The sneering eyes were glued closed, his nose tucked under his paws and the flat fox slept. The most life-like picture in a book of fairy tales.

And since that extraordinary Christmas Eve, children have been safe from the hunger of the flat fox. And they will always be safe, until the day when a careless person decides to open the book and cut him out.

Bill Buckley

BROADCASTER

THE IMPORTANCE OF CHRISTMAS

A million festive lights will flicker.
Two million relatives will bicker.
For every present that delights,
Two others are dismissed as frights.

For every family reunited,
Someone is left alone and slighted.
Sad smiles are worn, as lovers cleave,
By those the year chose to bereave.

Some children gasp at Santa's haul
Whilst others have no gift at all.
Whilst we eat more than we intended,
Black starving bellies grow distended.

And who, when all is said and done,
Believes the story of God's son?
How many go to Midnight Mass
Because they drank an extra glass?

And yet, tenaciously, we cling
To paper hats, that song by Bing,
The infant school nativity,
The drunken doze at half past three.

We need to, in a crazy age
That tears up every Rule Book page.
When every certainty has gone,
We dress the tree and soldier on.

When policemen have been known to lie,
When Yugoslavians fight and die,
When new diseases take the role
Of those we've battled to control,

When royalty falls into decay,
When Nigel, Michael, Rock are gay,
When grandma lives alone in fear,
When Bet no longer pulls the beer,

When politicians serve themselves,
Thank God for reindeer, sleigh and elves.
When change bombards us without pause,
We *must* believe in Santa Claus.

Katie Boyle

BROADCASTER AND WRITER

A CHRISTMAS STORY

The best Christmas present I ever had has caused me the most heartache, the most work and the most pleasure of any present I can remember.

It all started when we had broken up from school for the Christmas holidays and I had taken my hard-earned pocket money into town to buy presents for my mum, dad and little brother, Philip.

The queues for the bus home were long, the queuers crabby and the bus shelter non-existent, so I decided to walk back through the park.

I suppose you could loosely describe it as a 'white Christmas' in so much as a blanket of fog had settled over the town like a thick, wet, cold wad of cotton wool.

The park, as you can imagine, was deserted and so I was very surprised to hear a quiet whimpering sound coming from some prickly old bushes near the children's playground.

At first I thought I had imagined it, but no, there it was again. On closer inspection I saw a little brown nose appear from somewhere in the middle of the bushes, followed by a muddy leaf-covered form I could only assume was a dog. But a dog like I'd never seen before! The poor thing was so skinny its ribs were showing, and it was shaking all over.

Well, I've always been a softie for animals, although we didn't have any pets at home, so I whipped off my jumper, wrapped it around the dog, and went running off home as fast as I could with the dog joggling in my arms.

No one was about when I opened the back door, Mum and Philip were out buying *more* food and my dad was at work. I must admit I breathed a sigh of relief here, because something was whispering at the back of my mind that my parents would not be totally impressed with the sodden stranger. I wasn't too sure myself what to do now we were home but the dog looked so trusting and expectant that I decided to give it a drink and clean it up a bit.

After gulping down a bowl of water, the dog then enjoyed, or was subjected to, a dewberry-scented bubble bath. Surprisingly, this revealed not the dull brown I had been expecting, but a beautiful red and white coat (even though it was a little foamy). After a good rinse I thought, in my wisdom, that blow-drying would be a good move, as Mum was always moaning when I went around with wet hair. Looking back, I think I could have made a bad enemy at this point, particularly when the hot brush came out. The dog, however, just stood patiently and let me get on with it.

It was such a lovely little thing, all clean, dry and sweet smelling, with long floppy ears and a feathery tail.

Next stop was Mum's larder and being wise to neither the ways of dogs nor the ways of cooking, the menu for my guest was one of those tins of baked beans complete with mini-sausages. Well, at least I warmed them up.

The dog was grateful anyway. Ten chomps and slurps later and it was gone. Five minutes later, it was back, forcefully projected from the dog's stomach in a graceful arc, right on to the new dining-room carpet.

Of course, it was at this point that Mum and Philip came home, to a steaming, smelly, early present on a pristine Berber.

Mum completely freaked out, mainly because my grandparents were due within a couple of hours. But I'd like to think her sense of humanity shone through, because she did show some glimmer of concern at the emaciated form confronting her. A minor panic ensued, mainly concerning Shake'n'Vac, and I'm proud to admit that my sense of occasion made me play out the drama to the hilt, culminating in me, the dog, Mum and Philip at the vet's surgery within the hour. The vet, in her professional opinion, thought it was advisable to keep the dog (which was a girl) in for tests as she was in such a bad way.

Mum, I think, breathed a sigh of relief at this, because it meant we could be home in time for the arrival of the grandparents.

In the meantime I was warned that the cost of any treatment given to the dog would be taken from my Christmas money, pocket money and any other money I may come into the next fifty years or so.

I really didn't care. It was true that I'd put money by for things that I wanted, but the minute I saw that dog, it didn't matter any more.

That night I dreamed of having my own pet, and prayed that the police wouldn't find any owner that had lost a dog answering that description.

The next day we telephoned the vet, to be told that the dog was really just a puppy that needed a special operation on her stomach to let her eat properly and that might be why her owners had abandoned her.

This was the point where I really had to persuade Mum and Dad that the only thing missing from their lives was a dog, and that I would somehow or other pay for anything that the dog needed.

Well, obviously I was very convincing, or they were full of Christmas spirit, or something, but they eventually agreed that I could have the dog, provided that nobody claimed it and that I was going to be responsible for it.

All my saved money went on vet's bills and, of course, nobody seemed to want this little pup and, after her operation, she came home to us on Christmas Eve. By that time, Mum had butted in and seemed to know the right sort of food to give a dog.

This was probably just as well, because the dog never looked back to those baked beans and ate everything that was put in front of her.

Four years on, I now have a Saturday job to buy her food and pay for the yearly injections and anything else she might need.

The other day I saw a car parked outside the shop where I work with a sticker that said, 'A Dog is for Life, Not Just for Christmas'. I've never seen anything more true than that. It's all worthwhile when she snuggles up on my lap when I get home. She's my best friend. And her name?

It's Holly.

Well, it was Christmas, after all!

The Rt. Hon. Paddy Ashdown MP

POLITICIAN

I have so many fond memories of Christmas. But I think the most dangerous, most exciting and most memorable Christmas I spent was as a soldier, in the Brunei Rebellion in the middle of a mangrove swamp on the Sungci Lawas.

On 8 December, my wife and I had been at a party on a beach in Singapore. Somebody turned up and told us to return to camp, get into our combat gear, draw weapons and grenades and load ourselves on to an aircraft the following morning. I have never discovered a quicker way to get rid of a hangover! We were flown out first of all to the little island of Nabwan, and then on by twin-pioneer to a strip near a town called Lawas. The rebels were already in control of the town. Fortunately, we didn't face too much opposition re-taking it. I was then sent off into the mangrove swamps over the Christmas period to search for the rebels' leader, called Yassinefendi. We slept in parachute hammocks about the mangrove swamp at night.

The only thing I remember about that particular Christmas Day is having to shoot a crocodile at one stage and desperately trying to stop huge mosquitoes crawling into our sleeping bags!

In many ways it was also my worst Christmas. And even though it was memorable, exciting and as a soldier I can be proud, I can remember missing home a lot.

Sir James Savile Kt. OBE KCSG

ENTERTAINER AND MARATHON RUNNER

One of my most memorable Christmases I don't remember at all.

I was working down Waterloo Colliery in Leeds at the time and getting up at 4.30 a.m. ready for an eight-hour shift meant that at the end of the week you did not have all that much energy left. So, it came about Christmas time and the Duchess (my Ma) was away and I was at home alone. Christmas Eve was a good day. Out on the bike for a sixty-mile winter training run, back home and round to a couple of local houses for the mince pies and whatever was going and then, about 1 o'clock in the morning, off to bed.

A good wake up, stretch and let's see what Christmas Day has to offer, except it was Boxing Day because I had slept right the way through Christmas Day and Christmas night.

This created a mental complication because I was leaping about wishing everybody a Merry Christmas and it was only by accident, at 5 p.m. on Boxing Day, that I realized that it wasn't Christmas Day. It took some getting used to and I never really got over missing a whole Christmas Day.

Vince Hill

SINGER

THE ADVENTURES OF MR MAGIC MAN

A long time ago in a place called Greedy Land there lived a very special person named Mr Magic Man who was very unhappy.

You see, the people of Greedy Land didn't want him for who he was, just for the magic he could do.

So one day he decided he'd had enough of doing his magic for greedy people. He left his cottage in Greedy Lane and went off in search of a new home where no one would know of his magical powers.

He made himself vanish. Hey presto! One minute he was there and the next he was gone!

'How very nice,' he thought to himself as he journeyed from Greedy Land. 'I can just be an ordinary person and no one will know of my magic powers – except, of course, for those who really need my help.'

Mr Magic Man might have been tired of doing magic for greedy people, but he couldn't ignore those who deserved his help. You see, as well as being magic, he was also very kind and caring.

Before too long he met a lovely little dog called Lady. She'd been left in the woods by her owners from Greedy Land. They'd bought her for Christmas but couldn't afford to keep her, or so they said!

Mr Magic Man knew differently. 'Greedy people are also selfish people,' he muttered to himself as he stroked Lady.

She was now so weak and tired that she'd given up all hope, but with a wave of his wand and the magic word 'Abracadabra' Mr Magic Man made Lady happy and well again.

Lady was so small that Mr Magic Man picked her up, opened the lid of his huge top hat and placed her inside, where she was warm and comfortable for the start of their exciting adventure.

She yapped with joy as she joined Mr Magic Man on his search for a place where everyone was happy with what they had.

Soon Mr Magic Man and Lady reached the foot of a huge and beautiful tree and stopped for a rest. Mr Magic Man was so tired that his eyelids started to get heavier and heavier, and he was just dropping off to sleep when a voice boomed out:

'I wish I could fall to sleep!

'I've been standing here for a hundred years and I'm bored stiff!

'If only I could do something else or go to some other place.

'I wish I had legs like you.'

Mr Magic Man shot to his feet with a start and Lady scampered into the bushes in fright, with her tail between her legs!

The big tree was talking to them!

At first Mr Magic Man couldn't believe his eyes – or his ears for that matter – but, taking pity on the tree he said, 'What would you say if I could give you legs on which to walk?'

'I'd say tree-mendous, because I'd be tree-legged,' laughed the tree. 'But who's ever heard of a walking tree?'

'You're absolutely right,' chortled Mr Magic Man. 'Who on earth has ever heard of a walking, talking tree? It's too ridiculous for words!'

And with that he waved his magic wand, said his magic words and hey presto! The tree picked up his roots and walked!

Tree was so excited that he couldn't stop laughing. In fact, he laughed so much that his branches began to shake and his leaves started to fall off.

'You'd better stop doing that,' said Mr Magic Man with a smile. 'We're in for a cold night and I don't want you getting a draught up your trunk!'

Tree appreciated the joke (it was the first one he'd ever heard) and they laughed and talked all night. Next day Tree joined Lady and Mr

Magic Man on their journey, and what a trio they made: Mr Magic Man with a tiny dog named Lady sitting in his top hat, and a walking tree strolling beside him!

Their adventures took them firstly to Grumpy Land, where everyone moaned and groaned all day and thought only of themselves.

'Excuse me, but could you tell us the way to Happy Land?' enquired Mr Magic Man politely.

'Why do you want to know? Mind your own business,' the grumpy people moaned in unison. 'Get that scruffy dog off our streets and stop that moth-eaten tree dropping his leaves over our clean grass!'

'Thank you for your unwelcoming welcome,' said Mr Magic Man, who had now decided that the people of Grumpy Land were beyond the help of even his magic powers.

They had got so used to moaning and groaning that soon they could twin with Greedy Land.

'Greediness and grumpiness go hand in hand,' Mr Magic Man mused to himself as he, Lady and Tree headed off over the horizon to a place called the Land Of The Opposite Way.

It was a hard place to find, because although they'd seen the signposts they kept ending up where they'd started!

'We've got to go in the opposite direction,' said Tree. 'The Land Of The Opposite Way is the opposite way, if you see what I mean.'

Mr Magic Man and Lady were amazed at Tree's logic. 'You're absolutely right,' said Mr Magic Man. 'All the magical powers in the world can't beat sound common sense. Well done, Tree!'

And with that, Tree proudly picked up his roots and the threesome set off in the direction opposite to the signposts and soon bumped into a man who exclaimed: 'Goodbye! Day nice, isn't it? Hello!' before walking backwards down the street and falling up the kerb.

He couldn't see where he was going, only where he'd been!

Mr Magic Man, Lady and Tree knew they were in the Land Of The Opposite Way and suddenly Mr Magic Man realized that he might be able to help the poor, confused people.

He went to the mayor's parlour and knocked on the big wooden door. 'Get out!' boomed a voice from inside.

Of course, that means come in, Mr Magic Man thought to himself, so he opened the door and the three of them walked in, or rather Mr

Magic Man and Lady walked in! Tree was so big that his branches got caught up in the doorway!

The mayor was so surprised to see a walking tree that he fell backwards over his desk and backwards through his window! When Tree said, 'I'm very sorry', Mr Mayor was so amazed to hear a talking tree that he fell backwards through the window, back into his office and backwards over his desk and into the chair he was sitting in in the first place! The shock was so much that his hair turned from grey to black!

'This is amazing,' said Mr Magic Man to the startled mayor. 'We're actually in a place where everything happens the opposite way. How did it come about?'

'We've been witched by a curse,' said the mayor in his strange backward language. 'We lived in the past so much that our children had no future. So spell the witch put on us and everything we do is backwards opposite! We say things the round way wrong. Sometimes even our houses turn round while we're asleep and we all walk into the garden instead of the street. It's confusing very!'

'Let me help you,' said Mr Magic Man as he gathered together every magic thought in his head and waved his hands above his head in a flourish. 'Abracadabra, kalamazoo, be rid of the witch and turn the opposite to true!'

There was a huge puff of smoke and, as they all stared from the mayor's window the strangest thing happened: people in the street stopped in their tracks and started walking forwards. The hands of the huge Town Hall clock started to go the right way and everyone was waving and shouting good morning instead of goodbye.

It was a magic miracle, but no one liked it!

The people of the Land Of The Opposite Way didn't want to go forwards. They enjoyed going backwards, talking backwards and thinking backwards. They hated the thought of the future!

'I feared that this would happen,' Mr Magic Man said to the mayor. 'You see, I've already been in Greedy Land where everyone is selfish and uncaring. I've been to Grumpy Land, where everyone moans and groans all day long no matter what anyone does for them, and now I'm in the Land Of The Opposite Way, where the people can never see forwards because they're always looking backwards!'

And with that, Mr Magic Man threw his arms in the air and with another flourish, lots of magic words and another huge puff of smoke he turned everything back to how it was before.

With a heavy heart Mr Magic Man continued his journey with Lady the dog and Tree, feeling for the first time that no amount of magic could cure the world of its selfishness, greediness and lack of caring.

Soon they came to a land that was filled with sad children who, like Mr Magic Man, had grown tired of greedy, selfish people and those who couldn't see forwards because they were always looking backwards.

Tomorrow was Christmas Day, but because of the greediness, selfishness and lack of vision from their elders, the children had no presents to look forward to, no Christmas decorations and – worse still – no Christmas tree!

Try as he might, Mr Magic Man realized that he'd used up the last of his special powers in the Land of the Opposite Way. He was exhausted and couldn't help the sad children and he went to bed on Christmas Eve feeling sadder than he'd ever been before.

But something really magical happened, because within seconds of laying his tired head on the pillow he was in the Land of Dreams where he found a place called Happy Ever After.

It was a beautiful place in which everyone was happy and kind all of the time, the sun shone brightly all day long and it never rained, not even in winter!

It was the land for which he and Lady and Tree had been searching for so long. A wonderful land in which everyone had everything they had ever wished for.

Mr Magic Man jumped from his bed, popped Lady in the top of his hat, grabbed Tree by his nearest branch and together they led all the sad children to the town of Happy Ever After.

There was a lovely little cottage with flowers in the garden – yes, even in winter! They must have been Christmas roses! And Tree had never looked so wonderful. He had turned into the most magnificent Christmas tree that Mr Magic Man had ever seen. Hanging from every branch were colourful parcels containing presents for all the children, and Tree was covered in fairy lights from his top to his toe, winking and blinking in every colour of the rainbow.

Mr Magic Man sat and watched the children playing and laughing with the sheer happiness of simply being . . . children.

This was the real magic! Children enjoying their childhoods in a land filled with happiness and hope – with no room for greed, selfishness or backward thinking.

And to complete the magic, Lady was curled up contentedly at Mr Magic Man's feet, feeling warm, contented and perfectly safe.

'Everything was so perfect and peaceful,' Mr Magic Man thought to himself.

Tree would live happily ever after as a magnificent Christmas tree – surrounded by happy, laughing children who would never allow him to become bored with life.

Lady would live happily ever after surrounded by love and happiness – feeling wanted and cared for.

And Mr Magic Man would never need his magic again – he'd at last found a land where the magic was all around him. Mr Magic Man thought he might stay here for ever and ever. But how could he? He was in the Land of Dreams. This was all make-believe! Or was it? After all, Mr Magic Man really could do magic, couldn't he?

What do you think?

Lynda Bellingham

ACTRESS

STAR'S CHRISTMAS

The thing I like about Christmas in my house is the food. There is always so much of it. Usually I am only allowed to eat at mealtimes and there are never enough of those for me. I am always on the scrounge. Before we go any further I had better explain. I am a dog. A collie to be precise. My name is Star. I live with a lovely family with a father and a mother and two boys called Michael and Robbie. They are my best pals and we do practically everything together. One Christmas Eve, however, I had a very big thing happen to me all by myself. I will tell you about it.

It was Christmas Eve, as I have already told you. The boys and I had spent a great day hanging up decorations. Actually, I wasn't much help as I wanted to play and kept pulling things down. This made Michael and Robbie cross, so I decided to leave them to it and go and find my mistress, who was cooking in the kitchen. I knew that if I stood long enough and stared at her with my best sorry look she would give me something to eat. What luck! She was wrapping bacon round a huge bird. A turkey, I think it's called. I had a bit of that and then she got out some sausage rolls from the oven and gave me one. Delicious. Then I went back into the sitting room to find the boys were already changed into their pyjamas and had hung up their stockings as they always did on Christmas Eve. They usually hung one up for me too. I did not pay much attention because at that moment my mistress came in with a plate of jam tarts and a glass of wine. She put them on the hearth. For Father Christmas, she said . . . whoever he may be. When everyone had gone to bed I lay in my basket and had a think. Then it sank in that the boys had not hung a stocking up for me. I was very upset and when I am upset I get hungry. Then I remembered the jam tarts. I crept into the front room. It looked so lovely. There was this big tree all covered with fairy lights, which twinkled in the dark. From the branches hung huge shiny balls of every different colour. I went up and tried to sniff one. I got quite a shock I can tell you. There was another big dog staring at me from inside the ball! Then I realized it was my reflection. I am clever like that. My nose could smell the jam tarts above everything, so I trotted over to the fireplace. I only meant to take one. But, as I bent my head, a pair of black boots appeared before my nose. I looked up very slowly and saw a big red bump. On top of the big red bump was a round, jolly face with lots of white hair.

'What do you think you are doing?' he asked, not unkindly. I was so frightened I cowered behind the sofa. He put out his hand and called me over.

'Come here, old boy. I won't hurt you. You must be very hungry to pinch Father Christmas's treat.' He sat down on the sofa and stroked my head. He seemed to enjoy the tarts and the glass of wine. He laughed at me because I was dribbling (it's a very irritating habit of mine!). He broke off a piece of tart and gave it to me.

'Well I must get on with filling these stockings,' said the big red man. 'Where's yours then? Did they forget you? Dear, oh dear. We will have to see about that. Now, be a good dog and go to your bed. Happy Christmas.'

I did as I was told. I went back to my basket and before I knew it I

was fast asleep. I do not remember another thing until I was woken by Michael and Robbie shouting with delight in the other room. I leapt up and ran into the front room, ready for a bit of a romp. Well, what a sight met my eyes. All around the big tree were packets. Big ones, small ones, knobbly ones and squashy ones. There were piles of coloured parcels. I sat down with a bump and waited. What was going on? Suddenly, Michael held up a big stocking. 'Look, Star. This was left for you. It's yours!'

The stocking was filled to bursting with bones and biscuits and choc drops.

'We are so sorry that we forgot you, Star. But Father Christmas didn't. He brought you this.'

Father Christmas! Somewhere in my doggy brain that name rang a bell. Where had I heard it before? I just could not remember. But my nose told me it was something to do with jam tarts.

Michel Roux

CHEF

CHOCOLATE CAPPUCCINO MOUSSES

This easy dessert can be made a day or two in advance. If you like, you can add a dash of Tia Maria to the coffee cream, but I prefer it plain. The contrast between the unsweetened coffee cream and the half-set rich, sugary chocolate mousse is unique. For this you will need 4 shallow serving bowls or wide-mouthed, shallow cups 12 cm (4½ in) in diameter, 5 cm (2 in) deep.

SERVES 4
250 g (9 oz) plain couverture, or best-quality cooking chocolate
6 egg whites
125 g (4½ oz) caster sugar
4 egg yolks
150 ml (5 oz) whipping cream
1 tbsp instant coffee powder
1 tbsp unsweetened cocoa powder

1. Chop the chocolate with a chef's knife, place in a bowl and stand it in a bain-marie set over a medium heat. Remove from the heat as soon as the chocolate has melted.
2. Beat the egg whites until half-risen, then, still whisking, add the sugar, a little at a time and beat to a very firm snow.
3. Stir the yolks, then 50 ml (2 fl oz) of the cream into the melted chocolate and immediately fold in the beaten egg whites delicately with a spatula.
4. As soon as the mixture becomes homogeneous, divide it among the shallow bowls or cups and place in the fridge.

5. Just before serving, dissolve the instant coffee in a scant 2 tablespoons of water.

6. With a fork or whisk, whip the remaining cream into a light, runny foam, then add the coffee.

7. Top the chocolate mousses with the foam, sprinkle with a little cocoa and serve immediately.

Cleo Laine

SINGER

TOM'S BEST EVER CHRISTMAS

Thomas got his dream present for Christmas 1980, although he was not going to know this until that Christmas morning.

Thomas is my grandson, a very sweet, loving boy, who every year asked for the same gift whenever he was asked the question: 'What would you like best of all for Christmas, Thomas?' Why they kept asking him I could never figure out, as it was always the same answer: 'You know what I want more than anything in the world, and you always say I'm not responsible enough yet. So I'm not going to say.'

December 1980, and Christmas morning came around all too soon with all the hustle and bustle that families have to endure: the cooking, the tree, decorating, visitors, gift-wrapping and so on. It was so exciting for Thomas. Early on Christmas morning he woke up wide-eyed, full of expectations and wonderment. He was the first one up. He went into the family room where he knew the Christmas tree would be standing. It had been decorated the night before by his parents, so now it stood in the corner of the room heavily laden with the much-loved trinkets that were brought out annually from their hiding place under the stairs.

Thomas stood in his pyjamas gazing at the tree that had seemed so forlorn and wispy the day before, for this morning it stood sparkling and glittering with the baubles collected over the years

– dolls, Father Christmases and dated globes of the past. This year it had pride of place and seemed to be bigger than all the other years to Thomas. With a big grin from ear to ear he looked at all the packages placed underneath the branches. He noticed where his parents had placed the presents he had wrapped secretly in his room the night before, and approved of their position.

Then his eyes, still glancing around, fell on a large grey container with the biggest red bow he had ever seen in the world on top of it. But the big surprise was the writing on the bow, in such humungous letters that he could not help seeing them. It said: 'For Thomas, Xmas 1980'.

'Oh, boy! I wonder what that could be! I wish Mum and Dad would get up. I'm always awake before them on Christmas morning, and I have to wait so long before I get my gifts. Maybe I could just peek,' thought Tom.

Just as he was about to descend on the big-bowed container his mother came into the room calling out, 'Merry Christmas, Thomas, Merry Christmas', and gave him a big hug. Then she said, 'Let's get breakfast, shall we? And afterwards we can attack our gifts all together.' She knew she had come into the room just in the nick of time, but said nothing. Tom's face fell, but he knew there was no point in protesting. One by one the room filled slowly with other members of the family. Dad came in in his dressing-gown, all bleary eyed. 'Hi, Tom. Merry Christmas.' Then Chris, Tom's older brother, then Emily, his young sister, Grandpa, Auntie Beryl and Uncle Alec – and of course me. We were all buzzing with the possibilities the day might bring. Trying to get us to come to some sort of order, Tom's mother led us into the kitchen, where all hands helped to prepare the meal and lay the table. Tom's nose became aroused by the cooking and he announced that he was going to take a shower and get dressed before the meal. He thought it would keep his mind off the tree and all those packages the tree was protecting.

It really couldn't have taken his mind off it for too long a time, as he stepped in, got wet, soaped, rinsed and was out dried and dressed faster than any other morning of the year. When he arrived in the kitchen, brother Chris said, 'Boy, that was quick. You got a hot date, Tom?'

'Hey, no teasing on Christmas morning,' I said. 'Let's sit down and have a happy meal.'

The table looked very inviting, each plate having a small gift placed on top – which calmed Tom down, avoiding a squabble with Chris. Lots more greetings and thanks flew around the table as the carefully wrapped breakfast gifts were opened. Thomas could not make his out at all. It was from Emily and it was a bejewelled dog collar. He wasn't sure what to say to her and whispered to me, 'Did she make a mistake when she put the gift tag on? She does get things mixed up sometimes.' I said, 'I have no idea, Tom.' Thomas decided to accept the gift so that he did not hurt Emily's feelings. He decided that she had probably liked it so much herself that she thought he would feel the same. 'I'm going to put it on old Teddy. Thank you, Em. Ted will look better than he's done for years.' We all laughed and said what a great idea it was, pleased that the gift Emily had brought Tom seemed to have given him pleasure.

After all the breakfast offerings had been opened and everyone was happily full we all went into the family room, to be greeted once again by the glorious tree. When we had all settled down it was suggested that we should give Thomas his gift first, as he had been so splendid and thoughtful to his grandparents this year, helping in the garden without being asked and running lots of errands for everyone.

No one disagreed, with either the things Tom had done or the suggestion. I think Tom was a little surprised, as there was generally an argument about who was to go first. So Dad picked up the big grey container with the immense bow on top, turning it around to reveal that the front had a grid – and behind the grid was a fluffy ball that unrolled itself and started wagging an extra bit attached to the fluff. It looked surprisingly like a white puppy.

Thomas was speechless. His eyes were wide and filling with tears of joy. 'Well,' we all said, 'open it and meet your new friend. His name is Bentley, and he's yours to love and look after till he has grown and can look after you.' It all became so clear to Thomas – Emily's collar (that still ended up on Teddy's neck) and the container – so very obvious. 'What a dope I've been!' he said.

When he opened the container Thomas discovered a puppy dog who was no longer contained, had had enough of sleep and imprisonment, and was now ready to play with whoever wanted a game of lick and wiggle. So Thomas got hit with all Bentley's frustration on his release, with a good licking all over his face. It took quite a while before he could get his new charge to simmer down. Bentley was an English sheep dog, the sloppiest big ball of fluff Thomas had ever cuddled, and that morning they became the firmest of friends.

Thomas was given a list of instructions which he had to read and stick to if he was going to keep Bentley, the gift he had asked for every Christmas. The list contained Bentley's daily needs:

> He must be fed and watered
> He must be walked daily
> He must be brushed daily
> Trained to come when called
> – and to sit and stay.

Thomas tried hard to stick to these rules, and for most of the time – give or take a walk or a brush or two – he achieved his responsibilities. He and Bentley grew to love each other very much. The big red bow with 'For Thomas, Xmas 1980' on it became one of the prized Christmas treasures, brought out annually for Bentley to wear proudly around his neck.

In fact, whenever Thomas saw a big red bow after that – even in midsummer – it reminded him of his best Christmas ever.

Jean Boht

ACTRESS

A CHRISTMAS WEDDING

Sweet Emma Seglinde
Sat by the Loch
And dreamed of her Christmas Day joy

She'd known all her life
That she'd be the wife
Of Brian her sweetheart goose-boy

So long did she dream
The light turned to dusk
And the cattle had wandered too far

She ran in the dark
To search for the herd
And crossed into Forfaringar

'Twas the land of the Ferimoes
Feared by the Clans
Who knew how wild they could be

But the more that she called
With the mist and the black
The cattle she just could not see

Now what should she do
Remembering the tales
In her croft oft told round the fire

Stay still they had said
Keep warm till the morn
Make bracken and bog a safe byre

If the Ferimoes find you
They'll steal you away
And your ears and your nose will grow hooks

For beauty to them
Is not like to ours
Their magic can change form and looks

What now lay in store
As she hid in the bog
Poor Emma could never have known

For the King of this tribe
Knew she was the one
He wanted for his very own

She was good, she was kind
And he felt so alone
A kingdom to rule is so hard

With her by his side
Fair justice might reign
And the Ferimoes law would abide

So they caught her and tied her
With willows and rushes
Then carried her up to the Chase

Where the King sat and waited
'Till their work was completed
And the hooks had grown into her face

But try all they knew
With their spells and the Brew
Her nose and her ears stayed the same

For her heart was still tied
To the goose-boy at home
Still waiting for Emma his bride

So the King let her go
Made a friend not a foe
Of sweet Brian who tended the geese

And the Clans and the Ferimoes
No longer fight
For true love turned war into peace

Ellen and Derek Jameson

BROADCASTERS AND JOURNALISTS

LATE NIGHT SANTA

The Greenwich Mean Time pips signalled midnight as Father Christmas pushed open the doors of Studio 10 at Broadcasting House.

It had been a long journey from Lapland to the BBC's Scottish headquarters in Queen Margaret Drive, Glasgow.

Santa had tried to keep a promise to be interviewed live and exclusive on the Christmas Eve edition of the Jamesons' programme on BBC Radio 2.

Mind you, on this, his busiest night of the year, it was no surprise he was running late.

The studio was empty. The show was over. Everyone had gone home to bed – husband and wife presenters Ellen and Derek, their production team and the technicians.

Lucky for them, thought Santa. Truth was, even though the night was far from over for him, he was already hot, bothered and rather tired.

'Age catching up,' he muttered. 'No wonder, when I've just passed sixty-five – second time around.'

A sit down would be in order, he decided. Especially when he spied the food and drink kindly left out by the BBC canteen.

On second thoughts, he'd give the BBC coffee and curled-up sandwich a miss.

Just take the weight off his feet for a minute.

Making himself comfortable in a swivel chair in front of a great console of knobs and switches, Santa leaned back and put his big, black, shiny boots up on the desk.

The studio sprang to life as the heel of his boot activated the 'On Air' button.

Lights flashed and music filled the airwaves.

'Late night listening Radio Two,' sang out the chirpy, familiar station jingle. 'It's all for you on Radio 2.'

The high-tech electronic equipment clicked smoothly into operation.

An automatic turntable started spinning and Santa recognized his own signature tune, 'Santa Claus is Coming to Town'.

Excitement and panic jolted his brain into gear. As the music ended, Santa laughed out loud. One of his big, deep belly laughs.

'Ho, ho, ho.'

Catch-phrases of disc jockeys he knew and loved flashed through his mind: *Hello, there. See here, guys and gals. How's about that then? Welcome, pop pickers. Mornin', Mornin'. Do they mean me? Evenin' all.*

Hundreds of hours of radio listening combined to inspire and guide the BBC's newest recruit as he snatched up the music running order which had been left on the desk.

'Father Christmas here,' he boomed into the microphone, 'bringing you a festive mixture of music and chat to keep you company through this Christmas Eve.

'The next record is a particular favourite of mine – I Saw Mummy Kissing Santa Claus.'

For good measure he added his own side of the story. 'It's quite true. She did.' Santa chuckled jovially, enjoying the joke.

In fact he was enjoying himself enormously.

While the music played he did a little jig around the studio. He plonked a pair of headphones on top of his red hat and turned up the volume. The magic of radio.

As the last strains of the record died away, Santa leaned forward into the microphone, making sure his voice would be heard loud and clear.

'You're listening to the Father Christmas show here on Radio 2. Serving the public,' he told his unseen audience.

Addressing the nation is great fun, Santa thought to himself.

'What shall we do next?' he wondered out loud as yet another piece of Christmas music came to an end.

At that moment he spotted a sheet of paper headed: Questions for Father Christmas. Here was the chance to put the record straight!

'Tonight, live and exclusive here on BBC Radio 2, I shall reveal the man behind the beard.'

Warming to the subject, he declared, 'The secret life of the real Father Christmas, by the man who knows.

'Now it can be told. I was born in the Arctic Circle and raised by gnomes and elves. They designed the distinctive red cloak and hat I wear so they could always find me in the snow. Of course, I didn't have the long white beard then.'

Santa told the story of his life, leaving nothing out.

'The reindeer are family pets and Rudolph has always been my personal favourite. His red nose comes in very useful.

'There *is* a Mrs Christmas but she doesn't like the limelight.

'We have no children of our own because all the children of the world are special and important to us.

'And,' he paused for dramatic effect, 'contrary to popular belief, Christmas does not come but once a year.

'Christmas happens every single day. The Christmas spirit is one of love, joy and goodwill.

'My motto is: Everyone deserves some Christmas cheer, every day of the year.'

Santa surprised himself with the motto. He had just made it up off the top of his head. 'Rather good that,' he congratulated himself. 'Must write it down so I don't forget.'

Returning to the written questions, he added with a flourish: 'And finally, my favourite food is Christmas pudding with chocolate snowflake sauce.'

Santa ticked the last question on the script. He'd answered them all.

Time was running out. He must be on his way.

'We're coming to the end of the programme. Before I play my last record, a special message to each and every one of you.

'Santa loves you. Goodnight. Sleep tight.'

Father Christmas left the listeners to hum along to the Frank Sinatra hit 'Have Yourself a Merry Little Christmas' while he tiptoed out of the studio.

'This radio lark could become an annual event,' he smiled to himself. 'I'll be back same time next year – and maybe I'll find the Jamesons at home.'

Jeannette Charles

H.M. THE QUEEN'S LOOK-ALIKE

AM I DREAMING?

The days were very cold this time of the year, approaching Christmas; sometimes they were unbearable to Grandma, eighty-one years old and still enjoying life, but she did dislike feeling cold. Many times she would boil a kettle of water and fill a hot-water bottle which she put on her lap. It was so nice feeling warm and dozy in the afternoons. Her chair was near the window where she would watch the children go to school in the mornings. It reminded her of when she was a girl, when she rode to school on a horse – such lovely memories. She lived in a house which was surrounded by other houses, all alike. Privacy to her was important but, being a very friendly soul, she always had someone knocking on the door in the morning and later on in the evenings. This was to make sure she was well and, if in need of any food, one of her neighbours would buy it for her. Also, if ever she felt lonely she could, and did, knock on one of these kindly women's houses and she was always invited in. She felt lucky but Christmas was near and her only darling grandchild would be away with her mummy and daddy during Christmas visiting the other grandma. No good feeling sad, she thought, I will put on the radio and tidy up before my afternoon sit-down. Funny, I believed in fairies and I can well remember, when I was told there was no Father Christmas, I cried and cried. I wonder if any children believe in fairies, gnomes and the little people?

A sudden knock sent her hurrying to the door. It was Mrs Murphy. 'Mrs Noble, please could you have Kevin for me, as my husband has had an accident at work and is now at the hospital.'

'Of course, my dear. Off you go. I'll look after Kevin.' And so saying, she took hold of Kevin's arm and began to take off his coat whilst kneeling. Mrs Murphy went off and Kevin, a likeable little three-year-old, began chattering away.

That night Kevin was collected, still asleep, at about eight o'clock. Mr Murphy had suffered a heart attack and was to be kept in hospital for a while.

It was Christmas Eve. Mrs Noble was sitting by the fire. In the morning she would join the family next door but now she was very quiet with her thoughts. She heard a shuffle, a giggle and a little thud at her back door. Never had she felt nervous before, but what was it? She switched the light on at the back of the house and looked through the curtains, but all was quiet. With a lump in her throat she opened the back door but it felt heavy. She pushed again and slid out through the opening. There was a pile of presents which, after staring at it for a while and realizing she was very cold, she took into the kitchen.

One was a plain piece of tissue paper which had inside a most beautiful lace shawl. Who had sent it? There was no card, nothing. All the other presents had names on. Her heart was full of joy. How kind people are, she thought.

The next day dawned and on the dot of 11 a.m. she was knocking at the door of her host and hostess. Mr Murphy was home and feeling much better but he did need a lot of rest. Kevin jumped on to Grandma Noble's lap and never stopped chattering. It was a magical day: the food, the colours, the gaiety and happiness – truly the one day in the year that was different.

In the afternoon, she must have dozed off. She heard Kevin's voice saying, 'There is a real Father Christmas. Grandma Noble told me. She also said there were real little people who worked magic and I know that is true. Do you ever see fairies, Mummy?'

His mummy was very quiet and then said, 'Grandma Noble's shawl was made by the fairies. They know what a good lady she is.'

It was 4 p.m. There were lots of crackers on the table and everywhere there was colour. What a truly wonderful day this was.

On going to sleep that night, Grandma Noble heard a little voice say, 'There are fairies.' She clutched her shawl and said back, 'Thank you.'

Bob Wilson

BROADCASTER

A CHRISTMAS WISH COME TRUE

It was Christmas Day 1949. I was eight, football crazy, impressionable and a dreamer. Although born in Chesterfield, Derbyshire, the family tree sprouted no English branches. Parents, grandparents, great-grandparents *ad nauseam* were all fiercely Scottish. Kilts, sporrans and tammies were a familiar sight and I was never left in any doubt where my loyalties should lie. The blood coursing through my veins was pure tartan and I was proud of it.

Imagine my delight, therefore, when a present, opened that Christmas morning, revealed a blue goalkeeping jersey, roll neck and all. Blue for Scotland, of course. It was, and remains, one of my most memorable gifts. It was worn from that day on grass, concrete and sand. Every surface represented Hampden Park, traditional home of the Scottish International team. Eventually a mixture of wear and body growth rendered the jersey defunct.

Whenever and wherever I played, my ultimate goal was to appear for the country of my parents' birth when I grew up. It was a dream which, at the time, seemed highly unlikely. Why? Quite simply rules and regulations stated that a player could only represent the country in which he was born, which was, in my case, England.

So the dream, and the old sweater, had to be placed on the back burner. Any hopes of it being fulfilled were remote. Teenage years only added to the unlikely nature of my heritage dreams. In fact, I even came to represent England Schoolboys on several occasions, lining up alongside Nobby Stiles and, to my dad's horror, even playing *against* his beloved Scotland. He was happy for me and for my footballing progress, but seeing me help England inflict a 3–0 defeat on Scotland was too much to bear. Amazingly he never lost hope that I might one day, somehow, find a way to wear that Scottish jersey and win a Scottish cap.

Even at the moment of my greatest professional success, when my club Arsenal won the FA Cup and League Championship double in 1971, he was heard to utter, 'All I've really wanted was for Bob to play for Scotland.'

The why and how the rules for international qualification would be dramatically changed one month after that 'double' triumph escape me, but it happened. Suddenly there was a choice, if selected, of playing for the country of your birth or the nation of your parents' birth. The sequel to the decision was exciting and had fairy-tale proportions.

Scotland's manager of the time, Tommy Docherty, made me the first 'Anglo' to be selected. The opposition was Portugal – Eusebio and all – the venue, Hampden Park. The jersey lying on the dressing-room bench wore a badge which showed a lion and thistles and the words, 'The Scottish Football Association'.

Barely two months later, and before my second international appearance, my dad died, a proud Scot who'd had his greatest wish fulfilled and had seen his goalkeeping son's Christmas dream become reality.

Antonio Carluccio

CHEF

There was once a fly who was attracted to a cup of milk and was trying to get at it. Inadvertently the fly slipped over the edge of the cup and fell into the milk. The poor little fly thought this was the end of her. She began to flap her wings frantically to try and escape from the white liquid. In doing so for a while she noticed that the milk was slowly solidifying. Encouraged by this, she flapped her wings even harder and faster until all of a sudden the milk turned into butter and she was able to escape.

Never give up in life, somebody will hear your call!

BUSIE D'LA NONNA
(GRANNY'S LIES)

A Granny should not tell lies, but these particular ones are sweet lies, made from strips of pastry that are then cut into ribbons and tied in knots by a patient Granny. This dish can be eaten after an informal dinner, in the afternoon with a cup of coffee, or as a party snack. They are better if fried with pork lard.

SERVES 6

60 g butter

250 g flour

1 large egg

2 tbsp granulated sugar

5 tbsp sweet vermouth

a pinch of salt

pork lard or corn oil for deep frying

Mix the butter with the flour, as for pastry. Add the egg, sugar, salt and finally the vermouth. Knead into a smooth dough – this takes 5 minutes or so – the dough should be fairly stiff. Alternatively use an electric mixer that has a blade for dough making. Put the dough to rest in a cool place for 2 hours or more.

To make the *busie*, roll out the dough to a thickness of 3 mm. If you have a pasta machine, you can use it to roll the dough out into long strips of the right thickness. With a jagged pastry wheel, cut the dough into strips 2.5 cm wide and 20 cm long. Gently tie the strips into knots, like bows. Heat the lard in a large deep pan and when the fat is very hot, fry the bows 2 or 3 at a time until golden-brown, remove and drain on kitchen paper and allow to cool. Pile them up and sprinkle with icing sugar.

David Jacobs

BROADCASTER

I can see in my mind's eye a picture of Christmas morning when I was a child as clearly as I can see the paper upon which I write this short piece. It is not a particular Christmas, it is any one of those when I was between the ages of five and ten – for they all seem to be the same.

I shared a bedroom with my two brothers, John and Dudley, and as I was the youngest I went to bed before they did. I rarely went to sleep before they arrived and we usually had a chat before dropping off to sleep. I certainly didn't go to sleep before them on Christmas Eve.

We didn't hang up stockings: Mother would drape a pillowcase at the foot of the beds and, when sleep eventually came, dear, kind old Father Christmas would come in, take his tangerines from the pillowcases and put in our presents.

We would always wake up at about 4 o'clock and take a peep at the swollen pillowcases – generally overflowing with books and games.

At 6 o'clock we were allowed into our parents' room and we sat at the foot of what now seems an enormous double bed and excitedly opened our parcels. As I write I can even see some of the games and annuals.

After breakfast we would each make a selection of our own toys which we took to a local orphanage along with some specially bought new toys. My own children have always done the same and now my grandchildren do too. The circle is full and happy.

Alan (Fluff) Freeman

BROADCASTER

Dear Lovely Esther!!

I guess that this is not so much a Christmas story, because at this stage of the game, I will just about have survived sixty-eight of them, and they are very dim memories indeed!

I can remember waking up on a Christmas morning in my youth and discovering the miracle of a visit by Father Christmas and, to this very day, he has never forgotten me!

But what I can remember quite vividly is the chance I was given by the BBC in the Radio Department during the 70s.

I'd just completed ten years of *Pick of the Pops* on the Light Programme and Radio 1, and I was given an afternoon show five days a week.

All very lovely, I thought, but apart from playing records, I wondered just what else we could do with a whole ten hours.

We devised a slot called 'Get It off Your Chest' and I wondered if there might be any merit in finding time for some kind of slot devoted to youth. It was during this time that I met a quite wonderful lady by the name of Val Marshall who was connected with youth clubs and, after many meetings, we decided on a spot called 'Youth Club Call'.

Our thoughts were along the lines of: there were hundreds of youth clubs scattered all over the country, they all had many activities, but perhaps, because they were small clubs, they felt unimportant.

We decided that if they and their activities were mentioned nationally, they would feel a new sense of importance. Val and I visited youth clubs all over the place and the idea seemed to work quite well.

And when I look back on those years, I feel that our 'Youth Club Call' was all so worthwhile.

This, of course, all leads to your lovely self and the monumental work you and your team achieve with ChildLine.

I guess that all of us in our youth have those moments of uncertainty: we kind of get lost and don't quite know how to approach someone and unburden our problems on to them.

Anyway, Dear Esther, may you and your ChildLine team be allowed the opportunities to prosper further and to continually reach out and touch somebody's hand.

I spoke to Father Christmas last night, and he wishes you all a merry ChildLine Christmas! . . . All right? . . . Not 'arf!

Love

Alan Fluff

Max Bygraves

ENTERTAINER

In the early 1970s, I was appearing as Buttons in *Cinderella* at the London Palladium. The part of the good fairy was played by a talented dancer from South Africa. Her name was Juliet Prowse. She later went to Hollywood, made films and was escorted by Frank Sinatra for a while.

As I was walking towards the theatre, I met Juliet. We made our way towards the stage door just as large white snowflakes were beginning to fall.

Coming from South Africa, Juliet had not witnessed snow before; it was the first time she had seen the roads, rooftops and pavements that way. Suddenly the scene had changed from London Black to Christmas White.

Juliet stood there, letting the flakes fall on her upturned face, unconcerned that the matinee audience would be waiting to see the show. She was ecstatic. She turned pirouettes to get the maximum fall on her clothes, laughing merrily as I stood running on the spot to keep warm.

During the break between shows, we went out on the street again. By now the snow had settled and looked like a scene from Dickens.

To show Juliet how to slide and enjoy the winter snow, I took a run, hoping to slide a few feet along the ice. Unfortunately, I wasn't all that good. I tripped, fell and for the next two weeks had to limp on stage wearing an elastic bandage on my injured knee.

I haven't seen Juliet for many years but I'll remember that maniacal laugh of hers for ever.

Nick Owen

BROADCASTER

Warmest Christmas memories inevitably centre around childhood, when the fire was always roaring, there were carol singers aplenty, backed by Salvation Army brass, there was no pressure, only excitement, and, it seems in this misty reminiscence, there was always snow on the ground.

I particularly recall Christmas 1953, which indeed was whitish because I really badgered my kindly parents for a toboggan.

They were both teachers (of music and classics) at Berkhamsted School in Hertfordshire and were able to have one made for me in double-quick time at the school workshops. It was brilliant.

In the early hours of Christmas Day, my folks were woken by a piping six-year-old shouting, 'Bethlehem of Judea, he's been!' I went to a very religious school and that was the most pulsating exclamation I could dream up.

Mother and Father tottered in to discover that Father Christmas had indeed been and I was already marvelling at my wonderful, gleaming, bright red, wooden-slatted, metal-runnered toboggan.

We had to test it, of course, and at 4 a.m. on 25 December 1953 there we were, three-up, yelling Geronimo! We must have looked ridiculous but we can't be the only family who've done some daft things before dawn on Christmas Day.

That toboggan stayed with me for many years, surviving a hefty kicking from a milkman after I'd tied it to his milk float and followed him round town. Later I even chatted up my first girlfriends on it!

I finally gave it to the school and I am delighted to say that every winter the boarders there still dust it down for action. Look after it, boys – it's nearly an antique!

Patrick Moore

BROADCASTER AND ASTRONOMER

WISHING STAR

It had started out by being the worst day in seven-year-old Tim's life. As Mr Jenks, the vet, held up Tim's beloved black and white cat, Lucky, the news was clearly going to be bad. 'Tim, I'm sorry. Believe me, I've done all I can.'

Tim's lip quivered. 'You mean, Lucky's going to die?'

Mr Jenks put a hand on his shoulder. 'It looks like it. I'll come back in an hour, but you do have to be ready for the worst. I wish it were not so.'

Tim did his best to keep the tears back, but it was not easy; he stroked Lucky's head. Surely this must be a bad dream? 'I – I do know. Oh, how I want a Wishing Star!'

Mr Jenks looked surprised. 'What's that?'

Tim's father broke in. 'Oh, it was a story I was telling him last night – a star which comes down from the sky and grants the finder a wish. But it was only a story, Tim. You must know that.'

Mr Jenks went out; Tim held Lucky in his arms, and then, suddenly, he had a strange thought. 'Dad, I want to go outdoors – just for a few minutes. Look after Lucky, please. I won't be long.'

Tim's father nodded; there was so little he could say as Tim went slowly to the garden door, opened it and stepped outside. It was dark, and the stars shone down. Tim could make out the familiar shape of the seven stars of the Great Bear – and surely that was the Pole Star? With his thoughts still centred on Lucky, he wandered out across the lawn. 'It must be a dream,' he muttered. 'I can't lose Lucky. It would be too awful!'

177

Then, suddenly, he saw something strange. There was a flash in the sky, and a streak of light which seemed to come down some way in front of him. What was it? Tim broke into a trot. It seemed as if, well, whatever it was had come down in the field just beyond the garden hedge. It was still just light enough to see, and as he crossed into the field he could glimpse something glowing on the ground ahead of him. 'It – it must be,' he breathed, and stooped down. Sure enough there, in his hand, was a small circular object which shone pale green, and seemed to be warm.

Had it come from the sky? 'I saw it,' Tim thought, and carefully he handled the strange little globe. It seemed to be quivering; it was quite unlike anything else in the field – or anything that he had seen before. What should he do?

For what seemed a long time he stood there, holding the green globe. 'Are you really a Wishing Star?' he thought. He stared upward; all the other stars looked ordinary enough – and none of them moved.

Then he drew a deep breath, and held the globe tight. 'Give me my one wish. Make Lucky better – please!'

For a moment nothing happened. Then the globe seemed to swell out; there was a flash – and it was gone. Tim's hand was empty; nothing was left. Yet he was not frightened; there was, somehow, a feeling of friendliness about it all. He turned and made his way back to the house.

As he opened the door, his father came out of the dining room. 'Tim, do you know you've been gone for over an hour? We were just about coming to look for you. And I've something to show you.' He opened the door, and Tim saw Mr Jenks standing by the armchair. Then, without warning, he found a cat in his arms. Lucky had jumped up, and Tim clasped him. 'Is he ... is he ...?'

Mr Jenks sat down in the armchair. 'This is the most amazing thing I've ever come across. That cat was dying an hour ago – I would have been quite sure of that. Then, when I came back just now, well, there is absolutely nothing the matter!'

Tim's heart gave a bound. 'You mean he's all right? He's well again?'

'That's just what I do mean.' Mr Jenks

rubbed his forehead. 'I can't explain it, but all the trouble has gone. So far as I can tell, that cat will live for another twenty years at least.' He paused. 'Tim, where have you been?'

Tim cuddled Lucky; he had never felt happier. 'Dad, you were right about that Wishing Star. I, I found it.'

'I don't know what to say, but, well, all's well that ends well. You look tired out. Better go to bed. And take Lucky with you!'

Later, just before he went to sleep, Tim pulled Lucky close to him; Lucky purred softly. All was well. 'It was true,' said Tim sleepily. 'There are Wishing Stars. We know, don't we? We always will!'

Marje Proops

FRED

Let me introduce myself. I am very well-bred, a real aristocat actually, and I can tell you that living with *her* is not to everyone's taste. To start with, she named me Fred when I was just a kitten and too young and timid to put out a claw in protest.

Imagine it. Here am I, scion of a family of champions, with my ancestral line going back for generations, and she gives me a common name like Fred. She said, as she tried to soften me up with morsels of steamed cod, that my proper name, which is Comforts Cavalry Charger, was too much of a mouthful. She told me that shouting out Comforts Cavalry Charger over and over again to try to persuade me to stop chasing the squirrels and come home at once and go to bed, would drive the neighbours bonkers.

Between you and me, most of them are bonkers anyway. They coo in silly voices, 'Come on then, sweet little Freddie, come and say hello . . .' I turn on my four heels at such soppy blandishments. If they were to offer me a couple of sardines or a tasty bit of smoked salmon with a squeeze of lemon I might deign to respond to them.

Luckily there's one decent person in the neighbourhood – my mother-in-law to be. Her cat, Belle, is my girlfriend. I know I'll be marrying beneath me, for she is a mere moggy with no known parentage. She was a foundling, I understand, and was rescued from a Home for Wayward Cats or some such place by this kind person, my future mother-in-law.

Belle took my fancy because she is a fantastic looker – white, with black and ginger patches. She is also a very sparky puss, ready to have a go at anyone who annoys her, including her decent owner.

I have had severe words with Belle about this. 'It's no way,' I tell her, 'for a cat to behave. You'll have to do better than that if you want to stay in my good books.' Her response is to spit at me and bare her teeth and swish her luxurious tail and run up a tree in the garden. She knows I won't deign to follow her.

This person I live with says I am a bully, typically male, always giving orders and expecting females to obey my every command. She also remarks, as I close my eyes with boredom and pretend to go to sleep, that I'm too fat and lazy to walk ten yards, let alone run up a tree after Belle and give her the love and support a fiancée is entitled to expect from a top cat.

That's the pompous way this Agony Aunt talks. Can you imagine what it's like to be living under the same roof with her? Mind you, I know how to get round her. I've only to bestir myself and jump up on her lap while she's watching telly and purr for a second or two and she's all over me, promising to cook one of my favourite meals for supper, which is spaghetti bolognese, or a nice chicken casserole with plenty of carrots and thick, rich gravy.

She can call me Freddy boy (ugh) as much as she likes as long as I can get her to do gourmet food for me.

Sometimes, when I am particularly fed up with her for pushing me off my favourite chair just because it happens to be hers too, I go round to Belle's for a nosh-up. I am a firm believer in caring and sharing, although Belle gets a bit sniffy when I scoff her supper.

Sometimes Belle has an attitude. This worries me a bit when I contemplate the future with her. Could there, I wonder, be a trace of selfishness there? Doesn't she understand that women are meant, by nature, to do men's bidding? I have a feeling she may have been in secret counselling sessions with this Agony Aunt I've mentioned.

I suspect this person has put ideas into Belle's fluffy little head, ideas about equality between cats and all that rubbish, how it will be my job too, to chase mice. As if I'd do anything as undignified as chasing mice!

Belle has had a few tantrums lately. The Agony Aunt says she's showing spirit, which confirms my suspicions that Belle is being brainwashed. Only the other night, when I was sitting comfortably watching snooker on the telly, my favourite programme after soccer, she murmurs, 'Be nice to Belle, Fred. She's got a good heart as well as good looks.'

Of course my future mother-in-law agrees with all this woman talk. Wonderful, isn't it, the way these females stick together to make us males feel uncomfortable and guilty? Not that it cuts any ice with me.

I let them rabbit on (ooh! stewed rabbit, how delicious!) and give my dark grey fur coat a lick. I didn't mention, did I, that by birth I am a short-haired British blue? That is a very elegant thing to be, as I keep reminding my ginger and black and white girlfriend, giving her a playful tap with a silvery-tipped paw.

There is no call for her to respond with a flying tackle. Who does she think she is? Cantona? Or Gazza? Not that she'd recognize the names of my heroes. Now, she'd know who I was on about if I mentioned Oasis or Take That or some other outdated pop group she's so crazy about.

The appalling know-all Agony Aunt says couples should share common interests if they want to live peacefully together. The trouble with Belle is that, while I want peace, there's nothing she enjoys more than a bit of aggro. Perhaps I have made a mistake in choosing Belle to share my life with.

Maybe I should search the neighbourhood for someone as easy-going (*she* calls it bone idle) as I am. The trouble is I'd miss the little midnight snacks I tuck into after I've slipped through Belle's cat flap to have a go at her food bowl while she's still prowling around that tree.

But as this person I live with keeps saying, 'You can't expect perfection. You're never going to get it.' But she's wrong, isn't she? Belle's going to get purr-fection when I eventually find the energy to invite her to be my life partner. She's all set, is Belle, to live happily ever after when she becomes Mrs Comforts Cavalry Charger, which sounds a lot nicer than plain Mrs Fred.

I intend to go down on bended paws Christmas Eve and ask her to be mine. Then we'll both have a very happy Christmas – especially if you-know-who manages not to overcook the turkey.

A Special Thank You from Esther Rantzen

We've reached the end of the ChildLine Christmas book and, thanks to all our distinguished contributors, we now know the ingredients for the perfect Christmas. I thought long and hard as to whether my husband, Desmond Wilcox, and I could add anything from our own memories. There was one Christmas Eve fancy dress party when Desmond dressed up as a heroic Robin Hood, sadly his green woolly tights made everyone else guess he'd come as a leprechaun. Seeing him hoovering up afterwards, still in those tights, is one of the highlights of our marriage. Another recent Christmas Day lunch I brought out a dish of mayonnaise instead of the brandy butter, and smeared it over everyone's pudding. No – I don't think my memories will do anything to improve your Christmas festivities.

Instead, let me thank all the contributors and you, the readers, for so generously supporting ChildLine. We are also extremely grateful to Penguin for creating this book and making it the ideal Christmas present, especially our Editor, Luigi Bonomi, whose inspiration it was, and whose skills made it a reality.

Finally may I explain why your help matters so much. We know that ten thousand children try to ring ChildLine every single day – Christmas Day is no exception. We only have the resources to answer three thousand of their calls. We have to expand, so that every child can get through to our counsellors, to receive the comfort and protection they so desperately need.

Sometimes I feel overwhelmed by the enormity of our task. Then I remember the story of the starfish.

A man was walking along the coast in California – he rounded a rocky headland and found a beach where a freak wave had thrown millions of starfish up on to the sand. They were dying under the blazing sun. Far away in the distance a ragged figure was moving back and forth between the sea and the beach. Curious, he walked closer and saw that the man was patiently picking up starfish, one by one, and dropping them back into the waves. After watching a while he couldn't resist saying to the man, 'Why bother? There are millions of starfish on the beach, they'll be dead by noon, you can't possibly make any difference.' 'You're right,' said the man, as he continued to drop the starfish one by one back into the water. 'But I made a difference to that one. And to that one. And that one.'

I have a letter from a mother who tells me that ChildLine saved her son from committing suicide. He was being abused by a neighbour – a highly dangerous criminal who was attacking a number of children. Because of ChildLine's action, that man is now in prison. Without our counselling service, her little boy would now be dead. So we made a difference to that child. And to the other children who suffered along with him. And to hundreds of thousands of others who have been counselled by us. Thanks to your help, and this book, we will be able to make a difference to the lives of many, many more.

Merry Christmas.